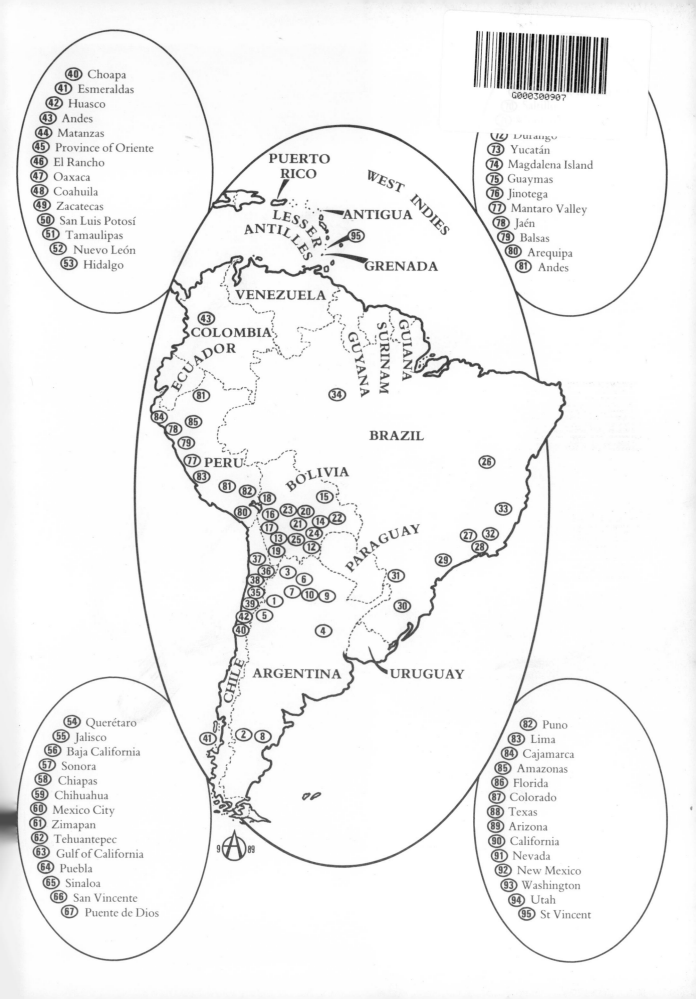

40 Choapa
41 Esmeraldas
42 Huasco
43 Andes
44 Matanzas
45 Province of Oriente
46 El Rancho
47 Oaxaca
48 Coahuila
49 Zacatecas
50 San Luis Potosí
51 Tamaulipas
52 Nuevo León
53 Hidalgo

72 Durango
73 Yucatán
74 Magdalena Island
75 Guaymas
76 Jinotega
77 Mantaro Valley
78 Jaén
79 Balsas
80 Arequipa
81 Andes

PUERTO RICO
WEST INDIES
ANTIGUA
LESSER ANTILLES
GRENADA
VENEZUELA
COLOMBIA
ECUADOR
GUYANA
SURINAM
GUIANA
BRAZIL
PERU
BOLIVIA
PARAGUAY
CHILE
ARGENTINA
URUGUAY

54 Querétaro
55 Jalisco
56 Baja California
57 Sonora
58 Chiapas
59 Chihuahua
60 Mexico City
61 Zimapan
62 Tehuantepec
63 Gulf of California
64 Puebla
65 Sinaloa
66 San Vincente
67 Puente de Dios

82 Puno
83 Lima
84 Cajamarca
85 Amazonas
86 Florida
87 Colorado
88 Texas
89 Arizona
90 California
91 Nevada
92 New Mexico
93 Washington
94 Utah
95 St Vincent

# CACTI

# CACTI

## Clive Innes

COLLINS

Frontispiece: *Espostoa senilis*

Text © Clive Innes 1990

First published in 1990 by
William Collins Sons & Co Ltd
London · Glasgow · Sydney
Auckland · Toronto · Johannesburg

A CIP catalogue record for this book
is available from the British Library

Produced by the Justin Knowles Publishing Group,
9 Colleton Crescent, Exeter, Devon EX2 4BY

Photographs: Peter Stiles and Clive Innes
Endpapers: Ethan Danielson

Typeset by August Filmsetting, Haydock, St. Helens
Printed in Portugal by Printer Portuguesa

# CONTENTS

# FOREWORD

For many years my interest has been centred on collecting cactus plants — trying to understand them and, perhaps even more important, to grow them successfully. But the need to 're-think' the Cactaceae and to grapple with the problems of nomenclature seems to occur far too often. There have been so many repeated changes in the naming, not only of the species but of the genera, that the cactus enthusiast might have considered investing in four-sided labels!

Serious consideration has been, and is currently being, given to try to remedy these persistent changes. Authoritative discussions have taken place — most recently at symposia at the Huntington Botanical Gardens in California and in Sicily — in which many of the foremost taxonomists specializing in this family participated. Many of the proposed generic changes were discussed and the most far-reaching were frequently challenged. Several revisions came under scrutiny, and eventually those names that were obviously acceptable, particularly to the amateur enthusiast, were retained. Nevertheless, the decisions have meant the disappearance or possible disappearance of a number of widely known names, including *Notocactus*, *Borzicactus*, *Machaerocereus* and even *Lobivia*, and many of the changes will be confirmed or rejected in the near future. However, the central purpose in this 're-naming' procedure was certainly accomplished.

In this book I have given the currently recognized names, together with those that *may* become absorbed into one or other genera; in addition, where necessary, I have indicated if a change is likely to occur. Also recorded is the botanical authority responsible for the generic identification or changes, together with appropriate dates.

This record endeavours to explain by means of this 'generic approach' exactly what the present status is of individual groups — for titles are being reduced from the 233 listed by Curt Backeberg to well under half that number, and if all the possible disappearances do eventually happen, the total of genera might well be approximately 90 or even fewer.

It is hoped that the information contained in the following pages will provide adequate guidance to the present position and sufficient information to enable cactus enthusiasts to anticipate the system that is likely to evolve for the genera of the Cactaceae.

*Clive Innes*

# INTRODUCTION

Numerous books have been written about the Cactaceae – the family name for cacti. Many references to the peculiarities of this form of plant life have occurred in literature since the early 17th century and continue to the present day. An extensive range of authoritative works offers guidance to the history, nomenclature, cultivation and general understanding of the vast number of species contained within this extraordinary family, but there is still a great deal to learn.

A genus *Cactus* was named by Carolus Linnaeus, the Swedish botanist and taxonomist, and within that genus he listed all the known species of the day. The generic name was undoubtedly derived from the Greek word *kaktos*, meaning a prickly plant, so the 22 different species contained in Linnaeus' new genus were limited to decidedly spiny varieties. Soon after this, Philip Miller, realizing how inadequate Linnaeus' single genus was, established four new genera. Since then botanists have investigated the unique characteristics of cacti and used their numerous features to separate one genus from another and to define different species within each genus.

## Cactus shapes

In general, one cactus genus appears very different from another. Many are columnar plants, sometimes branching from the sides to form large and tall tree-like plants; some attain 10 m (33 ft) or more in height, such as the giant saguaro *(Carnegiea gigantea),* so often featured as a typical cactus of the American deserts. Other species with erect, tall cylindrical stems produce branches from the base, eventually forming substantial and impressive clumps as is the case with such remarkable plants as the organ-pipe cactus *(Pachycereus pecten-aboriginum),* which is native to the Sonora desert in northern Mexico.

Several of the tall species, and a few of shorter growth, develop in maturity a dense crown of bristles and hairs called a cephalium. This woolly crown may cover a large surface on the upper part of the stem, as occurs with a number of columnar cacti; in other genera, such as *Espostoa,* with whitish bristles, the crown covers only one side of the stem, towards the apex, and is referred to as pseudocephalium. Perhaps the best known genus of cephalium-bearing cacti is *Melocactus,* the Turk's-cap cactus, in which the cephalium is centred on the crown of the barrel-shaped plant, remaining compact and low in some species, while others eventually grow to 20 cm (8 in) or more in height.

A vast range of cacti is globular or semi-globular in shape. Many are large, for example *Echinocactus* and *Ferocactus,* and they are usually heavily and fiercely spined; they occasionally form offsets, but most remain solitary, eventually reaching a height up to 1.5 m (5 ft), with a girth up to 45 cm (18 in). Many other cacti, particularly those from South America, including *Notocactus,* commence life as somewhat globular in shape, but with maturity they develop a more cylindrical appearance and not infrequently form offsets freely. By far the greater number of smaller growing cacti, such as

Opposite: cacti growing in Huntington Botanical Gardens, San Marino, California

*Gymnocalycium baldianum*

*Mammillaria, Rebutia, Gymnocalycium* and the like, have the habit of sending out new growths from the base or sides to form clumps. Some clumps remain comparatively compact, almost cushion-like, while others, such as *Echinocereus*, spread into loose clumps, occasionally into large mounds more than 45 cm (18 in) wide. At the same time it is not unknown for species within clump-forming genera to remain solitary throughout their lives.

The best known of all cacti are probably *Opuntia* species. These have thick and fleshy, cylindrical or rounded pad-like stems; the prickly pear, much encountered in southern parts of Europe where it has become naturalized, is just one example of some 400 species and varieties. The pad-like, somewhat flattened joints vary greatly between the species. This has resulted in several sub-generic names, which to a great extent help to associate plants with similar stem features: those with cylindrical stems and branches are included in the sub-genus *Cylindropuntia* if they are native to North America or in *Austrocylindropuntia* if the habitat is South America. The sub-genus *Tephrocactus* includes most of the smaller growing species, all of which were at one time recognized in a genus of the same name. There are other sub-genera, but that which involves most varieties is the sub-genus *Opuntia*, at one time called *Platyopuntia*. These cacti have oval or rounded pads and by far out-number those contained within other sub-genera.

A large number of other cacti could be comparable, being of globular form, including such rare genera as *Leuchtenbergia* and *Ariocarpus*, both of which have excessively long or wide tubercles covering the body of the plants completely. In their native habitat of the Texan and Mexican deserts, *Ariocarpus* species are completely below ground, only the tubercles indicating their presence.

It is often possible to establish the identity of a plant, at least generically, by its stem formation. This can prove a good starting-point when trying to give a name to an unfamiliar cactus. However, not all cacti inhabit arid regions, a large number being jungle plants. They are found principally in the rain-forests and other densely wooded areas of Central and South America, as well as in the West Indies. Here, stem formation is different and rather complex. Some have elongated strap-like stems and branches, either smooth-edged or crenated, some deeply as in *Epiphyllum*. A number of species have small flat segments, round, oblong or oval, each chain-like segment being linked to the next at base and tip, a characteristic very noticeable in *Schlumbergera* and *Rhipsalidopsis*, the popular Christmas and Easter cacti.

*Rhipsalis*, *Lepismium* and a few closely allied genera constitute a more complicated group. While a few species have stems somewhat reminiscent of the Christmas cactus, others consist of a series of flat, leaf-like joints, which can be almost intermediate between *Epiphyllum* and *Schlumbergera*. The majority of jungle cacti tend to have cylindrical stems, sometimes jointed, but invariably long and all comparatively smooth; a few are as thin as twigs, others of pencil thickness, and to complicate matters further, many genera have slender, angled stems, while others are fluted or twisted. Such complex genera have always been difficult to classify, and they have consistently been the cause of much controversy among botanists ever since they were introduced to cultivation. All jungle cacti would appear to be without spines, but nevertheless most are arrayed with short yet tough bristles or sparse tufts of very fine hairs appearing at intervals along the slender stems and branches or at the joints between segments.

Another group of cacti associated with jungle territory consists of clambering, climbing plants, in which the stem appearance varies according to genus. *Selenicereus* has elongated, rather cylindrical, slender and ribbed branches, which in some species can extend to 4 m (13 ft) or more in length. *Hylocereus* is equally long but with rather thicker stems that are 3- to 5-angled, rather wing-like. Both genera have aerial roots set along their lengths; they help to nourish the plants, at the same time anchoring the branches to trees or rock faces. All jungle species are generally considered epiphytes; they are not parasitic, gaining only support from the host trees.

## Cactus characteristics

Certain unique features distinguish cacti from plants of other families. All cacti are characterized by an areole, from the Latin *areola*, meaning a space marked out. The areole is a small greyish or brownish, cushion-like structure, sometimes white-felted and often hairy, which constitutes the growing point. Some areoles are larger than others; on some of the epiphytes they appear as mere dots. The areole is the place from which the spines and flowers emerge and the point from where branches or offsets develop. Where a particular species may bear leaves, for example *Pereskia*, or pseudo-leaves as in a few species of *Opuntia* (although they quickly shrivel and fall), these, too, come from the growing point, the areole.

Areoles are readily discernible on the majority of cacti. On *Pachycereus, Stenocereus* and other columnar plants with pronounced ribs, as well as such genera as *Ferocactus, Parodia* and *Notocactus,* the areoles are distributed evenly along the edges of the ribs, sometimes set well apart and sometimes crowded together. On *Mammillaria, Rebutia* and *Gymnocalycium* to mention but a few, the ribbed formations are emphasized by tubercles arranged symmetrically over the whole plant body, the areoles always in close proximity to the tubercles.

Areoles are dispersed in fairly regular formation on *Opuntia,* appearing over the surfaces on those species with flat, fleshy pad-like stems as well as on those with more cylindrical growth. *Opuntia* and related genera are distinguished by glochids; these are bristle-like barbs grouped together in small tufts in the upper part of each areole. Glochids readily detach themselves and easily get lodged in the skin, causing pain and discomfort.

On the leaf-like species of epiphytic cacti the areoles are usually set in the crenations along the margins of the flattened branches, especially apparent in *Epiphyllum* and *Disocactus.* Sometimes the areoles are scarcely perceptible, although they become more obvious as flower buds appear or a new branch begins to emerge. On *Rhipsalis* species, which vary tremendously in shape and size, the pattern of the areoles differs from species to species. With many of the slender, cylindrical and elongated forest cacti, the areoles can differ in size, some being very obvious, others resembling dots, so tiny that only a few wispy hairs denote the areole.

### Spination

Some authorities argue, probably correctly, that the spines of the cacti are actually reduced leaves, having evolved over millions of years, influenced by climatic and other environmental changes, from true leaves. They are modified leaves which, in the form of spines, provide a protective armoury.

The majority of cacti, certainly those from arid regions as well as a few from forest areas, possess spines. This characteristic serves to confirm the name *Cactus* originally given to them by Linnaeus when the selective word implied prickly plants, or more appropriately, spiny plants. The exact function of spines has yet to be determined, but in desert regions where mists and dews occur the spination can help to retain moisture and nutrients for a longer period so that the plants are better able to assimilate them within the body tissues. In addition, spines act as a defensive device against predators.

Whatever the practical value of spines, their variety of form is one of the attractions to cactus collectors. Many spines are straight, appearing as long barbs, while other species have a mixture of straight and hooked spines, particularly noticeable in *Ferocactus*. Perhaps the most beautiful are the comb-like multi-coloured formations adopted by some of the rarer, often miniature cacti within *Pelecyphora* and *Turbinicarpus*.

### Flowers
All cacti bear flowers. When plants are raised from seeds it may take a year or two, sometimes considerably longer, before flowers are produced, but with proper cultural care there is no reason why cacti should not bloom. Without flowers numerous species would have become extinct centuries ago, for they contain the reproductive organs that enable pollination to take place, resulting ultimately in the production of fruits and seeds. Flowers can and do differ in shape and size; they are usually borne on short stalks and the shape is often symmetrical; in others, such as *Schlumbergera truncata,* the flowers are zygomorphic, or symmetrical on one longitudinal plane only. Flower colours cover the whole range, except true blue and grass green, and come in various shades of white, yellow, pink, red and orange, frequently multi-coloured; all are enhanced by the contrasting colour of stamens and style, outstandingly displayed in many of the *Echinocereus*.

Flowering occurs from various parts of the plant bodies, often centred in clusters on the crown; on certain *Mammillaria* species the flowers encircle the crown and resemble a monk's hood. Many epiphytic cacti have large, frequently colourful and highly scented flowers borne at the tips of long or short tubes. The tube is a feature of many other cacti, but often the flowers are so small as to make the tube insignificant. Cacti are diurnal (day-flowering) or nocturnal (night-flowering); in some the display lasts for only one day, while others show their glory for up to one week.

### Generic and specific names
Common names are rarely used to describe cacti. Some, such as Christmas cactus and prickly pear, are popular terms, but in general it is inadvisable to use common names as they often refer to more than one species; for example, several distinct *Mammillaria* species have all been termed pin-cushion cactus. Botanical names are always preferable as they are internationally recognized. Generic names are of Latin or Greek origin. The genus is the first part of the name, while the second, specific, name describes the particular species. This denotes particular characteristics or refers to the area from which the species originates, and sometimes it recognizes the discoverer of the plant. The generic name always starts with a capital letter, and the specific name is always shown in lower case.

Since Linnaeus listed his 22 species, many plant discoveries have been made as more and wider landscapes become thoroughly explored. There has also been, and continues to be, much reclassification of cactus genera and species; this adds to the confusion on the part of amateur collectors who try to cope with the problems of changes in nomenclature. Since Linnaeus, many new systems have evolved, resulting in the number of generic names constantly fluctuating. In 1898 the German botanist Karl Schumann completed his thorough study of the complexities of the then-known species and

divided the Cactaceae family into three sub-families: Pereskioideae, Opuntioideae and Cactoideae, encompassing a total of 21 genera. In the 1920s, following their extensive exploratory expeditions, the Americans Nathaniel Lord Britton and his partner Joseph Nelson Rose compiled their famous four-volume work *The Cactaceae*; this covered 124 genera and a great many new species. In 1941 William Taylor Marshall, their fellow American, set himself the task of updating Britton and Rose and increased the number of genera to 139.

In 1966, Curt Backeberg, the famous German plant explorer and cactus enthusiast, published his mammoth work on cactus, and the subsequent *Kakteen Lexikon*, which was later translated into English. Here, after many years of fieldwork and research, he presented 233 genera. Backeberg will probably be best remembered for his obsession with splitting up existing genera in order to meet particular and minor characteristics. However, attempts were made shortly afterwards to reduce the number of recognizable genera. Although all of these proposals were not followed through, some botanists and taxonomists still favour reclassification of cactus species into fewer genera.

Species had suffered much the same fate. Just as a number of genera, previously accorded general acceptance, have been plunged into synonymity, so have numerous species, resulting in plants with only superficial likeness to one another being united under one specific name, although some may have been given botanical status as varieties or forms. Currently, fewer than one hundred genera are botanically recognized within the Cactaceae family, but species, with their varieties and forms, are numbered in their thousands.

Countless numbers of succulent plants are embraced in many other plant families, but those of the Cactaceae retain a prominent place in the minds and attention of collectors. Regardless of shape, size and habit, all cacti are indeed succulent plants, being endowed with moisture-storage tissues that enable them to survive and flourish in the most extreme dry and arid conditions. This fact has led to the erroneous idea that cacti require little or no water, even to the suggestion that they thrive on neglect. This is very far from the truth; they may survive but never thrive or flourish, their apparently inherited ability to accept weather privations and hardships notwithstanding. For good results, the amateur collector should treat all cacti with understanding.

There is rarely scope or opportunity for the cactus enthusiast to bring all species together under one roof. It is wise to indulge in segregation. Provide the sunniest places possible for desert plants, which need optimum light; species from jungles and rain-forests do better in a shaded location. If a greenhouse is their home, keep epiphyllums, species and hybrids, under the bench or in a specially prepared area for shade-loving plants; the same applies to cacti of epiphytic origin, whether grown in the ground, in pots or in hanging-baskets.

Opposite: *Wilcoxia albiflora*

Cacti belong to a distinct family of plants, and their cultural requirements differ enormously from those of most other plant groups. With only two or three exceptions, cacti are native to America, from the southerly regions of Canada, throughout the United States, Central and South America, to the mountains of Patagonia in southern Argentina. This fact alone will suggest that climatic conditions are decidedly complex. However, while weather conditions are remarkably variable according to locality, certain aspects have much in common: the number of light hours is more or less constant throughout the year, in itself important for growth. Rainfall is much less predictable, with certain regions having fairly regular wet and dry seasons. Many areas, especially those in parts of Mexico and Central America, however, have infrequent rainfalls, which are often sparse, and months, even years, can pass without rain so that semi-desert conditions develop. In such extremes cacti must sustain themselves on the vigour and nourishment accumulated within their bodies during more favourable periods, the only additional benefit being derived from the mists or dew so often in evidence during night hours in arid countries.

In their wild habitats, cacti have by nature been bequeathed certain indispensable features that enable them to develop and sustain growth and that encourage the production of flowers and subsequently the fruits with their seeds. They thrive and develop due, to no small extent, to the composition of the soil whose important ingredients, we, in turn, must endeavour to provide for cacti in cultivation. Temperature is another factor playing an important role for cacti in their natural habitats. Day temperatures are quite likely to soar, in periods, to humanly unbearable heat, yet night temperatures fall rapidly to the opposite extreme. However, in general, winter and summer temperatures are reasonably predictable; the colder months providing a rest or dry season; with the onset of the warmer weather, cacti burst into activity, often encouraged by periodic outbursts of rain followed by prolonged periods of dry weather.

Not all cacti grow in desert regions; many species, commonly known as forest or jungle cacti, enjoy much the same environment as orchids, bromeliads and other forest plants. They are mainly true epiphytes, lodging in the forks of trees with rotted leaves entangled in their roots. Other species are of climbing and clambering habit, their roots firmly set in the soil, at least initially; then they spread their branches and gradually ascend the tree trunks by means of aerial roots, frequently losing their footholds in the ground and becoming totally epiphytic. Some of the forest-dwelling cacti are saxicolous, that is growing on rocks, with their roots fixed rigidly to the rock face, though still having the protection of the jungle. Frequent rains, heavy dews and almost persistent mists are the lot of rain-forest cacti, whose fine roots readily absorb moisture, feeding it to the stems and branches of the plants. They do not rot for the simple reason that no water is retained around the roots and drainage is rapid with subsequent aeration. Rain-forest cacti are not parasitic; they take no nourishment whatsoever

Opposite: *Echinopsis huascha*

from the living cells of the trees upon which they are lodged and use them merely as an anchorage.

A number of species, notably opuntias, from regions where severe cold often grips the countryside and plants are not infrequently covered with snow, may be considered hardy in many parts of Europe, including Britain. The successful culture of outdoor cacti requires very porous soil, preferable on slightly sloping ground, and the cacti must be placed in a position where they will have a degree of protection, such as an over-hanging roof, preferably on a south-facing wall where they can gain the maximum light.

In cultivation, it is impossible entirely to emulate the natural habitat. Nature never intended plants to be imprisoned in pots or grown under glass or in the confines of the home. However, this is the only recourse open to those fascinated with cacti, and for the successful cultivation of these plants it is essential to provide them with the best possible growing conditions.

## Compost

The most suitable growing medium for cacti has been the subject of controversy for many years; guidelines can be suggested, but ultimately the decision largely rests on the grower. Whatever the compost, it is essential that the mixture is porous, for cacti from jungle regions as well as for those from semi-deserts. Many commercially prepared mixtures are available from garden centres, and a few are specially formulated as cactus composts. Other preparations are based on the John Innes compost formula with No. 1 and No. 2 probably being the most suitable. Soil-less (or loam-less) composts are also readily available; they contain sufficient fertilizer to sustain plants for a period. However, with these, it is particularly important to add a quantity of washed gritty sand in the proportions of two parts of soil-less compost to one part sand. All commercially prepared composts may be less porous than desirable, so examine the chosen mixture carefully to make sure that it allows good drainage. You can, of course, prepare your own compost. Good sterilized loam is not readily available, but if it can be procured, use the following formula: one part sterilized loam; one part sifted, well-decomposed leaf-mould; one part washed gritty sand; plus a sprinkling of base fertilizer, and ideally a little well-rotted cow manure. It is essential that you should know your plants and where they originated. A number of desert plants grow on calcareous slopes and can often be identified by having whitish spines and hairs, such as *Mammillaria plumosa* and *Cephalocereus senilis*. All such plants need the addition of limestone chippings in the compost. For jungle plants, it is advisable to increase the leaf-mould content to one and a half parts, with a slight increase in the quantity of sand.

## Potting

The choice of containers is very much a personal one. Clay pots have gone out of favour, being replaced by plastic. For the majority of cacti, clay or plastic pots are equally suitable, provided that they are clean and of the correct dimensions for the occupant. Under-potting can be calamitous, and too large containers are equally unacceptable; large pots become applicable

*Escobaria tuberculosa*

only as plants grow and demand more space. The bottom of the pot should be covered with broken crocks or small gravel to allow better drainage; charcoal added to the drainage layer will help to prevent souring of the soil in the container. This applies to plants set in individual pots as well as to several placed together in a bowl garden; for the latter, make sure that the chosen plants require exactly the same soil mix and attention.

## Light

Light, of varying degrees, is essential for all plant growth. Desert cacti need the sunniest and brightest position possible, such as a south-facing window-sill. Lack of good, direct light inevitably proves to be to the disadvantage of the plants; they are likely to lose their peculiar characteristics, becoming etiolated and rarely succeeding in producing flowers. Indoors, even the sunniest light comes from one direction only, so it is advisable to turn the pots regularly so that all sides of the plants receive the light.

Cacti from rain-forest areas require different siting. Set them in a shaded place where there is no likelihood of direct sun; filtered light, out of the direct path of sunlight or shaded by net curtains or Venetian blinds, suits them best. Many of the epiphytes are ideally suited for hanging-basket culture, but again they should be out of direct sun.

## Temperature

Obviously, indoor temperatures cannot be adjusted to suit individual plants. During the summer months, normal room temperatures are suitable, and in winter the majority of cacti will settle for a happy minimum. It is never wise to coddle plants, and during the winter season, when most desert cacti enter a period of dormancy, temperatures of 8–10°C (46–50°F) will prove sufficient. The exceptions are desert cacti from extremely hot habitats, such as certain species of *Melocactus*, *Discocactus* and *Uebelmannia*, which should be given a warmer situation, with about 15°C (59°F) as the minimum. Once the rest season is over and plants are being brought back into active growth, temperatures can be allowed to rise without concern, with due attention being given to watering.

The majority of epiphytic forest cacti flower in winter and early spring and therefore need higher winter temperatures than dormant desert cacti. Ordinary room temperature is suitable provided that air humidity is increased with overhead sprays of tepid water; do not let the temperature fall below 10°C (50°F) during bud formation and flowering. Once flowering is over, forest cacti should be given a short rest of about three weeks when they will put up with a temperature of 8–10°C (46–50°F) and reduced watering.

## Watering

Cacti are constructed so as to be able to withstand drought. They have the ability to take up water during rainy periods and store it in the tissues, thus enabling them to go through the dormant season in completely dry soil. They are sustained by this stored nourishment at all times, both developing and storing up while in active growth in the rainy season, then drawing on their built-in reservoir during long intervals of dry, hot weather. In cultivation the same guidelines should be followed: during the growing season, water thoroughly, literally soaking the soil, then allowing any surplus moisture to drain away. Do not water again until the soil is completely dry, then give another good soaking. Repeat throughout the growing season until late October, when most desert cacti enter their dormant phase. The exceptions to this rule are cacti from forests and jungles. In summer they can follow the same watering regimen as desert cacti, though the soil should never be allowed to dry completely between watering. However, as the epiphytic species tend to produce flowers from late winter to late spring or early summer, it is imperative that the soil is always kept just moist so that the roots are not permitted to dehydrate.

*Never* give small doses of water at frequent intervals 'in case the soil gets dry'. *Never* leave the containers standing in water once the soil is saturated. Failure to adhere to these rules is likely to mean that the plant will rot at the base, and with most species that is fatal.

## Feeding

Whatever compost is used, in pots or in outdoor or greenhouse beds, it is inevitable that nourishment – mineral salts – within the compost becomes exhausted. This applies particularly to pot culture. It therefore becomes necessary to replace the nutrients with regular supplies of fertilizer during the growing season, from late April to late September. Numerous excellent commercial brands are on offer, most of them general fertilizers containing nitrogen, potassium and phosphorus in various proportions. However, cacti need more than that; trace elements of iron, magnesium, copper, boron, manganese, cobalt and molybdenum are important nutrients.Comprehensive fertilizers containing these extra nutrients, some of them especially prepared for cacti growing, can be located at large garden centres and specialist nurseries.

Feeding should generally be undertaken every three or four weeks and is best done in conjunction with watering. Always use the dosage recommended on the container; liquid fertilizer or a powder that can be easily dissolved in water is the easiest to use. Failure to carry out a proper feeding programme can lead to retarded growth and few, if any, flowers with those that do develop being of poor quality.

## Propagation

The enthusiastic cactus grower can extend a collection of cacti by several methods. Initially, he may purchase plants in flower or in full growth, but it is possible to increase a collection by other, perhaps more exciting and certainly cheaper procedures.

### Seed propagation

Raising plants from seed is neither difficult nor complicated. It does not necessitate expensive or elaborate equipment, merely adherence to certain rules in order to achieve success. First, it is imperative that fresh seeds are obtained. There is every reason to presume that cactus seeds remain viable for two, maybe three years, but there is no guarantee for every species. Fresh seeds are offered by many specialist nurseries and are usually from named species, which is an added benefit. Mixed seeds, which may include species of several genera, with some seeds being large while others are dust-like, can cause problems.

The best time to sow is early in the year, from late January until late March. Use a John Innes seed compost or a mixture of two parts sifted peat with one part fine, gritty washed sand. Spread it evenly in a seed tray, moisten and firm it well, then sprinkle the seed finely over the surface. Small, dust-like seeds require no covering, but larger ones should be covered with sifted gritty sand to about their own depth.

The seeds can be germinated in a heated propagator. Otherwise, put the tray in a large polythene bag; seal it and place it in a fairly dark, warm place where a temperature of 22°C (72°F) can be maintained. Germination may take only a matter of days, although some species are likely to take much longer. When the seedlings appear, gradually expose the container to more light, but not full sun. At the same time allow air to circulate to avoid any possibility of damping-off, a disease that affects seedlings if too humid an atmosphere is permitted at an early stage. Wherever possible, let the seedlings remain in their trays for at least three months, by which time they are likely to be large enough to prick out individually into other containers. From then on, if a temperature of 21°C (70°F) can be maintained, they may be grown on throughout the winter period, given very careful watering and always good, indirect light.

*Vegetative propagation*

If only a few plants are wanted, vegetative propagation is an easier and quicker method of increase, particularly in the case of those desert cacti that have a natural tendency to form offsets. Others can be propagated from cuttings taken from side branches of tall-growing cacti, from the stem pads of *Opuntia* and allied genera, and from the jointed stem sections typical of *Epiphyllum* and others of similar growth habit.

Offsets are produced around the base of *Mammillaria, Rebutia, Lobivia* and the like; they almost invariably have roots already. Remove the offsets, pulling them away from the parents with a pair of tongs or severing them with a sharp knife, taking care not to damage the roots. Plant the offsets singly in small pots and treat them as mature plants, giving them perhaps a little more care.

Cuttings are best taken during the summer months. Use a clean, sharp knife to sever the cutting at a natural joint, be it from the side or base of a branching cactus, or a stem or pad section from a jointed species.

Allow the cuttings to dry off for a few days or until a callus has formed over the cut surface. Set the cuttings in pots or pans containing a mixture of two parts peat and one part sharp washed sand; place them shallowly, if necessary supporting the cuttings with small sticks. Leave them to root in a warm, shaded place; an occasional spraying with tepid water will help to prevent both compost and cutting from drying out. It is often advocated that a hormone rooting powder promotes root formation on cuttings, but while this is often effective with many other plants, it has no value with cactus cuttings that have been allowed to callus.

*Grafting*

This technique should be resorted to only when cacti prove difficult to grow on their own roots or when it is the only method by which to maintain an unusual growth form such as a cristate *Mammillaria wildii* and a few of the *Cerei*. Red, yellow or whitish forms of *Gymnocalycium* and *Lobivia (Chamaecereus)* have become popular; colorations, due to a lack of chlorophyll, generally become noticeable at seedling stage. As long as they continue to gain sustenance from the cotyledons, the seedlings survive, but once the cotyledons shrivel, the seedlings, too, will die. The idea of grafting – and perpetuating – such coloured mutations was an inspiration of Japanese horticulturalists in the late 1950s. These grafted cacti have become extremely popular, especially with non-collectors. In this instance, grafting as a propagation method is the only means by which such bizarre seedlings can ever survive.

Grafting should be carried out during the growing season, never during

Opposite: a group of cristate cacti

dormancy. The best period is probably from mid-May until late July; this gives sufficient time for the union of scion and stock to mature before the approach of colder weather. Grafting consists of uniting two different but compatible plants, joining a piece of stem or a seedling (the scion) of one species to the rooted stem (the stock) of another cactus.

A number of sturdy, fast-growing cacti can be used as stock plants, such as species of *Echinopsis* (including *Trichocereus*), *Hylocereus*, *Selenicereus*, *Opuntia*, and *Pereskia*. Young plants tend to make better stock, or one-year-old cuttings of *Selenicereus* or *Pereskia* if these have already developed a strong root system. Whatever the choice, the stock plant should be healthy and growing well. For grafting to be successful the stock should be as wide or slightly wider than the scion, more so when desert species are concerned. Use a sterilized, very sharp knife and select a bright, warm place in which to work; this will go a long way towards ensuring a successful result. Avoid too long a stock, or the ultimate grafted plant could look very uncharacteristic as it grows larger.

Make a straight cut across the stock and bevel the edges of the ribs slightly. Prepare the scion in the same way, with a clean, straight cut and a slight trimming of the edges, before sliding the scion carefully on to the cut surface of the stock. Make sure that the inner core or vascular rings of both scion and stock match, because it is here that the union takes place. The scion must be held firm to the stock by means of rubber bands crossed over the top of the scion and underneath the stock. Place the grafted plant in a warm, bright place but out of full sun; after two to three weeks the union will probably be accomplished. Remove the rubber bands once you are certain the operation has been successful; continue to keep the plant shaded from full sun for at least another two weeks, by which time the scion should be showing signs of new growth. It can then be treated normally.

There are several methods of grafting. The one described above is known as the flat graft and is one of the easiest. Grafting of more slender species, such as *Schlumbergera*, involves a different process known as a cleft graft. Many collectors aspire to having a spreading, tree-like Christmas or Easter cactus, and to achieve this a longer stock, to give a semblance of a trunk, is required. Suitable stocks are found with *Selenicereus*, particularly *S. macdonaldiae*, or *Pereskia*. In either case, the best stock is a well-rooted cutting of strong growth that has been cut to suit the purpose. Use a tool of razor-blade sharpness to cut the stock plant to the desired height, then make a vertical slit down the centre of the stock to about 2.5 cm (1 in) deep. Prepare the scion by trimming away the skin from both sides and tapering it towards the base so as to form a wedge about 2 cm ($\frac{3}{4}$ in) long; insert the scion into the cleft, ensuring that the vascular rings of both are in contact. Keep the graft in place with a long slender cactus spine, pushed horizontally through stock and scion; they can also be bound with soft nylon tape if desired. The union will take about 3–4 weeks; the plant will need a position out of full sun, more shady than for the flat graft, and should ideally be kept at a temperature of about 21°C (70°F).

Never water grafted plants, or even spray them, until you are convinced that the union has taken place.

**Pests**

Successful cultivation of cacti depends on other factors than soil, temperature, watering and fertilizing. All efforts made to build up a fine collection of plants will be futile unless close attention is also given to the presence of pests or diseases. Problems are bound to arise, even with the best managed collection, and many unwelcome insects are liable to infest cacti. Systemic insecticides have become a recognized method of controlling the spread of pests. Commercially branded preparations are readily available for application in liquid form. A dilute systemic insecticide should be watered on to the plants, at the dosage recommended on the bottle; this filters through to the root system, the roots absorbing the insecticide, which is then transmitted throughout the body of the plants, causing the demise of any pest that feeds off the tissues. Three or four applications during the growing season are recommended. It is also possible to deal with individual pests as they occur, provided that you are able to recognize them and the symptoms of the damage they can cause.

*Mealy bugs*

One of the most pernicious and destructive of pests, mealy bug resembles a small woodlouse covered completely with a white, woolly wax. The eggs are contained within the white tufts and the young usually form colonies near the adult. They all feed on the sap in plant tissues, weakening the plants and encouraging diseases. As soon as a minor infestation is observed, dab the patches with methylated spirit applied with a small paintbrush. Otherwise, treatment with an insecticide containing malathion will help to eradicate the pests, if it is repeated every two weeks.

*Root mealy bugs*

Somewhat similar to mealy bugs, root mealy bugs are unfortunately not so easily seen; their presence is first denoted by poor or retarded growth. They suck the roots of cacti; removing the plant from its container will quickly reveal these white-coated pests, and they can often be seen adhering to the sides of the container. Eradicate them by washing the roots completely clean, removing every particle of soil in the process, then soak the root system in a malathion-based insecticide to ensure that all pests are destroyed. Repot in clean soil and a fresh container.

*Scale insects*

Resembling miniature limpets, brown or greyish-brown in colour, which can form thick encrusted colonies, scale insects lay eggs under the scales, and, after hatching, the larvae crawl away to find a suitable place to feed. They become immobile, form new scale colonies and in turn lay eggs. The earlier this pest is discovered, the better. They can be removed at an early stage with a brush dipped in methylated spirit; once the scales harden, however, it will be a matter of thorough treatment with an insecticide containing malathion.

*Red spider mites*

These minute reddish creatures are almost too tiny to discern. They form colonies and gradually become surrounded by very fine webs. They suck the sap of plants, which begin to turn a brownish colour and generally develop distorted growth. Too dry an atmosphere, especially in a heated greenhouse, is likely to lead to infestations; good ventilation and fresh air, with adequate humidity, will help to deter the problem. If attacks are noted, spray thoroughly with an insecticide specially formulated for the purpose, or use a malathion-based spray. Give three or more applications at three-day intervals until the pest is totally eradicated.

*Aphids*

Aphids, whitefly, greenfly and a number of similar creatures may cause problems, all of these insects feeding on plant tissues and often covering them with a sticky honeydew. Repeated applications of a systemic or non-systemic insecticide will usually clear the problem. Perhaps the most damaging is the sciarid fly, which is chiefly associated with peat-based composts or with leaf-mould that is not thoroughly decomposed. They are tiny greyish flies, which lay eggs in the compost, where the small white grubs feed on roots of young and older plants alike. Remove the plants from their pots and soak the roots thoroughly in a malathion-based insecticide to destroy the grubs completely.

**Diseases**

Many of these are self-inflicted, caused by poor hygiene, incorrect watering or lack of ventilation or failure to eradicate pests. One shows itself by a blackening of the base of the stems, bacteria having invaded the plant tissues and turned them black and soft. It is often due to wrong watering – a cactus left saturated without means of drainage is a likely victim – even more so if the compost has too high a nitrogen content, as can happen with excessive doses of nitrogenous fertilizer. If the problem is not too pronounced, the blackened portion can be cut away and the wound treated with sulphur powder; it is important that every trace of the trouble is removed or it could easily occur again. Fungicides such as benomyl and quintozene can act as deterrents.

A reddish discoloration of plants may be the result of incorrect watering. *Never* water overhead in the heat of the day as drops of water can lodge on the plant bodies and often form reddish spots. Brownish cork-like marks developing near the base of certain cacti may be caused by irregular watering or by extremely humid conditions; globular desert species are most likely to be affected in this way. Cultural conditions should be improved.

Opposite: cacti growing in Huntington Botanical Gardens

# THE GENERA OF THE CACTACEAE

This Directory is not intended as a comprehensive thesis on the Cactaceae, nor does it seek to enumerate the thousands of species, varieties and forms contained in the family. Rather, it records the genera that, according to present-day thinking, constitute the total number necessary to encompass all cacti species. Taxonomists now propose that the cactus family should be reduced to 85 recognized genera, and in this process many familiar generic names will become obsolete, some perhaps without full justification. A number of reputable and long-standing names, generally acknowledged and appreciated by cactus enthusiasts, would appear to be worthy of retention and are included here.

The Directory covers 117 genera, which are organized in alphabetical sequence. It details the origin and history, habitats and principal characteristics of each. Representative species are listed under each genus, with descriptive details of the characteristics that distinguish one species from another.

Unless otherwise stated, the species described are day-blooming and flower during late spring and summer.

## ACANTHOCALYCIUM

The genus was created by Curt Backeberg in 1935 for a group of South American plants. They are similar to *Lobivia*, but because the flowers have a circle of hairs, formed from modified stamens, around their base, they appeared to deserve a separate generic status. The hairy feature is emphasized in the name, which is from the Greek *akantha*, meaning a prickle or thorn, and *kalyx*, meaning calyx; it would also seem to refer to the papery scales of the calyx where those near the top are modified into spines. However, current research has decided that the genus is dimorphic and suggests that some species are close to *Echinopsis*, others to *Neoporteria*; it is likely the species will eventually be transferred to other genera and the present name cease to be operative. The few plants involved are particularly attractive, more or less globular in shape with many ribs arranged symmetrically and with large colourful flowers. All are easy to grow, requiring a rich, open compost, free watering in summer, but to be kept dry in winter. A sunny position is advised as this will encourage flowers. Keep a minimum winter temperature of 10°C (50°F). All grow readily from seeds.

### *A. aurantiacum*

Discovered and named by Walter Rausch, this is native to the Catamarca region in Argentina. It is something of a squat plant, being about 9 cm (3½ in) wide and only 5 cm (2 in) high. It is greyish-green with up to 16 pronounced ribs carrying well-spaced areoles armed with about 5 long radial spines approximately 3 cm (1¼ in) long. The flowers are a bright deep yellow, about 5 cm (2 in) long and wide, the inner petals frequently a much deeper shade.

### *A. violaceum* (syn. *Echinopsis violacea*)

According to E. Werdermann, this is a taller plant, growing to about 20 cm (8 in) high and 13 cm (5 in) in diameter, rather pale green with a very spiny crown and about 15 notched ribs with areoles set some 2 cm (¾ in) apart. There are about 12 radial spines, slender and spreading, yellowish and tipped brown which are about 3 cm (1¼ in) long, and 3–4 slightly longer central spines. Trumpet-shaped flowers appear from near the top of the plants, with golden yellow stamens and style; they are a clear pinkish-violet, about 6.5 cm (2¼ in) wide, when fully open.

## ACANTHOCEREUS

This genus was established by Britton and Rose in 1909; it had earlier been designated as a sub-section of that name, in the genus *Cereus*, by A. Berger. It seems likely that *Dendrocereus* will eventually be deemed synonymous. There is also a close affinity with *Peniocereus*. This interesting and unusual group of plants extends in habitats from Florida in the United States, through Central America to Brazil in the south. The generic name comes from the Greek *akantha*, meaning thorn, which describes the very spiny formations along the stems and branches. They are shrubby, free-branching plants, often of climbing or clambering habit, and with ribs that form almost angular growth. The nocturnal flowers are large and attractive, and are followed by oval, red fruits, mostly quite spiny, with a few blackish seeds set in a reddish pulp.

The genus contains 10 or more species, but with only a few exceptions they are almost unknown in cultivation. The plants require a bright location, out of direct sun;

warmth is important, the more so as they enjoy a degree of humidity throughout the year. A winter temperature of about 15°C (60°F) is advisable, and occasional light misting with tepid water will benefit the plants. Use a rich, fairly acid compost, which must be permeable; water freely from May to September, but thereafter give just sufficient water to prevent the soil from drying out completely. For successful cultivation feed with a weak liquid fertilizer every 4–6 weeks throughout the growing season.

## A. pentagonus

This is the type species and is undoubtedly the best known of the genus. It is one of the original 22 species listed by Linnaeus and named by him as *Cactus pentagonus* in 1753; about 20 other synonymous names exist. It is found in Florida, Texas, Mexico and Central America and is also recorded in the West Indies. Stems may be erect or more frequently clambering, especially in the

*Acanthocalycium violaceum* (syn. *Echinopsis violacea*)

natural habitat, they are often up to 3 m (10 ft) or more in length and branch abundantly. They are 3- to 5 angled, deep green and to 8 cm (3 in) thick. The areoles, which are set well apart, are greyish in colour with 6–8 awl-shaped, brownish-grey radial spines, 1 cm ($\frac{3}{8}$ in) long, and one or more much longer central spine to 5 cm (2 in). Flowers are borne on long, spiny, woolly tubes; they are approximately 20 cm (8 in) long, and they have greenish outer segments and white inner petals; the short stamens and style are white; the stigma lobes are a creamy-white colour.

## A. colombianus

Britton and Rose described this as a tall erect plant with stems branching into two, all branches being three-angled and about 9 cm ($3\frac{1}{2}$ in) thick. Spination is a matter of extremes – the 5–8 radial spines are almost minute, while the one or two central spines are very thick and up to 6 cm ($2\frac{1}{2}$ in) long. The white flowers are 25 cm (10 in) long, with thick floral tubes. It is a native of Colombia.

# ACANTHORHIPSALIS

Above left: *Acanthocereus pentagonus*; above: *Acanthorhipsalis monocantha*

A small genus of epiphytic plants, the title was initially accredited to Karl Schumann and subsequently confirmed by Britton and Rose in 1923. The generic name, from the Greek *akantha* meaning a thorn, refers to the spiny stems, which distinguish this genus from its close relative *Rhipsalis*. It does, perhaps, constitute an uncertain genus; the type species, *A. micrantha*, has been transferred by Myron Kimnach to a new genus, *Lymanbensonia*, and taxonomists are now proposing to unite *Acanthorhipsalis* with *Lymanbensonia* and *Lepismium*.

The genus includes possibly 4–5 species. All have flattened or three-winged joints, the margins being slightly crenate with spiny areoles set at intervals along their length. The flowers, which appear in winter, are borne in profusion from the lateral areoles, followed by rounded berry-like fruits. All are native to South America.

All species are of easy culture, requiring a rich, readily draining soil mix with plenty of decomposed leaf-mould added. A semi-shaded position is advisable, with minimum winter temperatures of around 10°C (50°F); the soil should be kept just moist throughout the year. Propagation is preferably by stem cuttings taken after flowering.

## A. monocantha

Originally described by Heinrich Grisebach as a *Rhipsalis* in 1879 and later included in this genus by Britton and Rose, this Argentine variety is the best known and deservedly popular. The stems are mainly thin and flat, frequently reaching to 60 cm (2 ft) or more in length and about 2 cm ($\frac{3}{4}$ in) wide; the areoles are white-felted with one or more rather yellowish spines. Flowers are whitish, borne singly from the side areoles, each about 1 cm ($\frac{3}{8}$ in) long. An even more colourful, close relative, *A. monocantha* var. *samaipatana*, which is native to Bolivia, has bright, wax-like orange flowers approximately 1.5 cm ($\frac{5}{8}$ in) long. The small berry-like fruits are rose-pink and persist on the stems for quite a long period. This variety was discovered by M. Cardenas, an eminent Bolivian botanist, and given its present status by Curt Backeberg.

## A. crenata

Discovered by Nathaniel Britton in Bolivia, this variety has rather shorter and wider stems, but is in general appearance very similar to the above, except that the flowers are bright red. It was formerly included in the genus *Hatiora*.

# ANCISTROCACTUS

This is another of many genera whose present status is very much in doubt. It was established by Britton and Rose in 1923, with three species being reclassified from *Echinocactus*. The generic name is from the Greek *ancistron*, meaning hook or barb, possibly referring to the hooked central spines, a feature that is also apparent in *Sclerocactus*, with which it could well be united. Plants are native to Mexico and Texas. Species are very few in number, mainly globular or short cylindrical, with deeply furrowed ribs, which are tuberculate, and with distinctive hooked central spines. The flowers appear in or close to the crown of the plants. They are of fairly easy culture in a normal cactus compost, given regular watering throughout spring and summer and a liquid feed every three or four weeks. Keep the plants dry from November to April. Propagation is from seeds.

## *A. scheerii*
This, together with *A. megarhizus* (which is now considered to be a form of *A. scheerii*), was the first to be classified within the genus. The plants are about 12 cm ($4\frac{1}{2}$ in) tall and 7 cm ($2\frac{3}{4}$ in) in diameter, the 13 ribs are tuberculate, slightly spiralled, with areoles bearing 15-18 spreading radial spines about 1 cm ($\frac{3}{8}$ in) long and 3–4 central spines, the lower one strongly hooked, often to 5 cm (2 in) in length. All are yellowish-green and about 3 cm ($1\frac{1}{4}$ in) long. *A. scheerii* f. *megarhizus* has a pronounced tuberous rootstock; it bears 20-24 radial and 4 central spines of yellowish-brown. The flowers, too, are yellowish, and 2 cm ($\frac{3}{4}$ in) long.

# APOROCACTUS

A well-known and deservedly popular genus, which was established by Charles A. Lemaire in 1860. The exact meaning of the name is difficult to determine; it is derived from the Greek *aporos,* meaning tangled or impenetrable, but seems to make no acknowledgement of the principal feature, the trailing stems and branches, which have won for the genus the common name of rat's-tail cactus. It was initially recorded as being vine-like, creeping or clambering and at that time included two species that might well have met with this description but they were subsequently removed to other genera.

All the species at present included in the genus are slender-stemmed, trailing or pendent in habit and furnished with aerial roots. Flowers appear on more mature growth, most frequently near the lower part of the stems. In cultivation they require a really bright position, although full sun is not essential; in fact, full midday sun can cause scorching. A rich, open compost is important; water freely during the flowering and growing periods and give an occasional light, overhead spray with tepid water during dormancy. A winter temperature of 10°C (50°F) is sufficient. The best containers for these species are hanging-baskets, which allow for a graceful fall of the branches and a splendid display in the centre of the plants when the flowering season is in progress. All species are from Mexico and possibly South America. Propagate by stem cuttings.

## *A. flagelliformis*
The best-known species and one of the 22 species Linnaeus described in 1753 as *Cactus flagelliformis*, it was subsequently renamed *Cereus* by Philip Miller in 1768. The specific name is from the Latin, meaning a whip, which is perhaps more suggestive of the common name currently in use. The stems are slender, 1–2 cm ($\frac{3}{8}$–$\frac{3}{4}$ in) thick and are capable of attaining well over 1 m (3 ft 3 in) in length. They have 10–12 rather inconspicuous ribs with close-set areoles bearing 15–18 brownish, yellow-tipped spines. Flowers are 7–8 cm ($2\frac{3}{4}$–3 in) long, deep rose-pink, the inner petals slightly spreading, with the outer petals reflexed, somewhat similar to flowers of *Schlumbergera* species. The habitat is uncertain, but the species seems first to have been brought into cultivation from Peru, although it is commonly seen as a garden plant in Mexico.

The crossing of this species with *Heliocereus speciosus* has produced the plant known as *Aporocactus mallisonii,* or *Cereus smithii* as it was first named.

## *A. leptophis*
Although this has similar stem features to the above, there are only 7–9 ribs, which are slightly wavy-edged. It was placed in this genus from *Cereus* by Britton and Rose. The name, from the Latin *lepto*, meaning slender, and *ophio*, snake, correctly describes the appearance of the stems. The areoles are white and velvety, with up to 14 spines, which are purplish at first, then becoming yellowish, about 4 mm ($\frac{1}{8}$ in) long, and soft to the touch. The flowers, 4–5 cm ($1\frac{1}{2}$–2 in) long, have bright red outer petals while the inner are rose-pink with a distinctive violet median line; stamens are pale pinkish-red. This is an epiphytic species from forest areas of southern Mexico.

## *A. flagriformis*
This is found in Oaxaca in southern Mexico. The stems are slender and elongated with 7–10 ribs, with areoles set further apart than in *A. flagelliformis*. Spines are yellowish-brown, and consist of 5–8 radials and two or more centrals, the latter often to 1 cm ($\frac{3}{8}$ in) long. Flowers are 8–9 cm ($3$–$3\frac{1}{2}$ in) long, deep rose-pink, often paler along the edges of the inner petals. The stamens are red, and the stigma-lobes white.

### A. martianus

One of the most uncommon species of the genus, *A. martianus* is found in central Mexico and has also been recorded from Oaxaca. Stems are elongated to more than 1 m (3 ft 3 in) in length and 2 cm ($\frac{3}{4}$ in) thick, with about 8 low ribs, often less. Areoles occur at 1 cm ($\frac{3}{4}$ in) intervals and are very prominent, with 6–8 brownish radial spines, about 12 mm ($\frac{1}{2}$ in) long, and 3–4 centrals, which are more bristly. The flowers, about 10 cm (4 in) long, are rich scarlet with a narrow purplish margin to the petals. The rather similar *A. conzattii* has 8–10 ribs with closer-set areoles and 15 or more spines of unequal length. Flowers are orange-red with white stamens and a slender white style about 6 cm ($2\frac{1}{2}$ in) long. It was discovered by Professor C. Conzatti in Oaxaca in 1912 and named in his honour.

A number of excellent cultivars have become available in recent years, chiefly resulting from hybridizing *Epiphyllum* cultivars with *Aporocactus* species. Among these, the following are outstanding: 'Cascade', many

### Aporocactus flagelliformis

large shell-pink blooms produced on long, slender stems; 'Karen', large pinkish-orange flowers with deep midribs. 'Najla', very large orange-red flowers of particular charm; 'Orange Queen', long 'tails', bearing large, pure orange flowers.

# ARIOCARPUS

This is one of the most extraordinary and fascinating genera of the Cactaceae. The title was raised by M.J. Scheidweiler in 1838, and since then the generic names *Anhalonium*, *Roseocactus* and *Neogomesia* have been made synonymous with it. Only six species are recorded, and all comprise some of the most sought-after plants of the family. The name is derived from the Greek *aria*, meaning haw, and *karpos*, which refers to fruit, in this instance particularly to the shape and colour of the fruits. These curious plants all have something of a gnarled appearance due to the rough character of the large thick

Above: *Aporocactus flagriformis*; above right:
*Aporocactus* 'Karen'

and triangular tubercles that cover their entire surface. All species are to all intents and purposes spineless, although on *A. retusus* very small, insignificant spines can sometimes be observed at the tips of the new tubercles. The rootstock is a taproot, often quite thick and fleshy, and the plant body, which in habitat is invariably set well in the soil, is more or less globular in shape. The species are native to Mexico and south-western parts of Texas. In cultivation they require the sunniest position possible, especially as the funnel-shaped flowers usually appear in late summer or autumn. A truly porous compost is essential, perhaps even more so than for most other cacti. Careful watering is required; avoid at all times excess moisture remaining on the surface of the plant, so water around the cactus rather than over it. Keep completely dry during the dormant season and maintain a minimum temperature of 10°C (50°). Propagation is by seed.

### A. retusus

A Mexican plant and found in parts of Coahuila, Zacatecas, San Luis Potosí and elsewhere, *A. retusus* is the type species of Scheidweiler. Since the description was first presented, it has been the subject of many name changes. The specific name is indicative of the peculiar shape of the tubercles. The plant is more or less flat and can develop a spread of 15 cm (6 in) or considerably more in cultivation. The whole rounded body is completely covered with large, thick, three-angled and greyish-green tubercles, which are quite hard, and are often about 2 cm ($\frac{3}{4}$ in) or more long, generally with a woolly areole on the upper side near the tip. Flowers appear from the woolly centre of the crown; they are pale-pink or whitish, measuring 4 cm ($1\frac{1}{2}$ in) across when fully open. They are day-flowering, lasting for several days.

### A. agavoides

Still remembered under the earlier name of *Neogomesia*, which was given by M. Castaneda in 1941, this unusual species was found in Tamaulipas. It resembles a miniature *Agave*, as indicated in the specific name. The species was transferred to *Ariocarpus* by Dr E. Anderson in 1962. A small plant, only 4–6 cm ($1\frac{1}{2}$–$2\frac{1}{2}$ in) wide with long, widely spreading greyish tubercles about 4 cm ($1\frac{1}{2}$ in) long and 6 mm ($\frac{1}{4}$ in) wide, it is easily mistaken for something other than a cactus. Areoles occur on each of the tubercles and sometimes bear a few short spines; the flowers are large and impressive, to about 4 cm ($1\frac{1}{2}$ in) across and a rich deep-pink in colour.

*Ariocarpus retusus*

### A. trigonus

Perhaps the largest-growing species is *A. trigonus*, which was transferred to this genus from *Anhalonium* by K. Schumann. It can become very wide, to 20–30 cm (8–12 in), and has numerous greyish-green or yellowish-green, semi-erect tubercles to about 5 cm (2 in) long, flat on the upper surface, keeled below and pointed at the tips, with a single areole near each tip. Yellowish flowers appear from the centre of the plant, to 5 cm (2 in) across, with whitish stamens, style and stigma lobes.

# ARMATOCEREUS

This genus consists of about 10 species of South American plants from the Andean regions of Colombia, Ecuador and Peru. Raised by Curt Backeberg in 1935, the name comes from the Latin *armatus,* meaning armed, and probably refers to the spiny character of the stems. All are columnar plants, some rather tree-like, others in fairly dense, bushy clumps. The flowers are nocturnal and appear close to, or at, the tips of the stems. Many of

the species currently recognized were formerly included in *Lemaireocereus,* a genus that is now obsolete. All are of easy culture; they succeed in either sun or partial shade and a minimum winter temperature of 7°C (45°F) is quite satisfactory as long as plants are kept dry. Normal cactus compost meets their needs, provided that it is permeable. Feeding every 4 weeks with a weak liquid fertilizer is advised from May to September; this will stimulate growth and encourage flowering. Propagation is best from seeds sown between January and March.

### A. laetus

Previously registered as *Cactus laetus* by Humboldt, Bonpland and Knuth in 1823, this was then referred to *Cereus* and *Lemaireocereus* before its transfer to *Armatocereus* by Backeberg. This tree-like plant – it grows to about 6 m (20 ft) high – comes from Central Peru and Ecuador. It has many bluish-grey branches, which have pronounced constrictions indicating the growth of pre-

*Ariocarpus trigonus*

vious seasons. The prominent ribs are broad and deep, 4–8 in number, with areoles set at regular intervals of about 3 cm (1¼ in). Each bears one to three awl-shaped, brownish-grey spines to 8 cm (3 in) long. The flowers, from near the tips of the stems, are white, about 8 cm (3 in) long and 4–5 cm (1½–2 in) across. Fruits are very spiny and green with black seeds.

### A. godingianus
Named by Backeberg and described by Britton and Rose as *Lemaireocereus* in 1923, this also is a tree-like plant, growing to about 10 m (33 ft) high in its native Ecuador. It has a woody trunk, 30 cm (1 ft) or more thick, and many jointed, greyish-green branches up to 9 cm (3½ in) thick. These have 7–11 ribs, with small areoles bearing numerous small slender spines up to 4 cm (1½ in) long. Flowers are about 10 cm (4 in) long with 2 cm (¾ in) long tubes, short white petals and brownish bristles set densely on the floral tubes.

### A. cartwrightianus
Named as *Lemaireocereus* by Britton and Rose, this is one of the better known species. It was transferred to *Armatocereus* by Backeberg in 1935. It is native to Ecuador and Peru. Tree-like, growing to 5 m (16 ft 6 in), it has many short branches, 15 cm (6 in) thick. Large brown-felted areoles bear about 20 blackish spines, to 2 cm (¾ in) long. Flowers, about 8 cm (3 in) long, have reddish outer petals and small whitish inner petals. It is a shade-loving species.

# ARROJADOA

This interesting genus was named by Britton and Rose in 1920 in honour of Dr Miguel Arrojado Lisboa, a plant explorer in Brazil. Initially the two known species were placed in the genus *Cereus* by Dr A. Gürke until the new name was adopted, and following this, Curt Backeberg decided that the species were so close to *Cephalocereus* as to be inseparable, although *Arrojadoa* was retained as a sub-genus. Currently the species have regained generic status, and several new plants have been discovered. It would also appear that the genus *Micranthocereus* and that of *Floribunda* are synonymous with *Arrojadoa*.

The principal feature distinguishing this group is the pseudocephalium. In other genera, the pseudocephalium becomes the terminal crown of a plant and remains so, but in the species of this genus it takes the form of a lateral ring or collar, so that the new stem section protrudes through its centre to form yet another pseudocephalium as the growth matures. All known species are native to Brazil, mainly from fairly arid country. In cultivation they offer few problems, although a minimum temperature of about 13°C (55°F) should be provided to keep plants content. The compost must be very porous; any retention of moisture can prove detrimental even in the growing season. Allow the compost to dry out completely from mid-October until late March; keep the plants in the sunniest position possible. Propagate by seed or by cuttings.

### A. penicillata

A native of Bahia, Brazil, this was one of the first species to be discovered, and it was recognized under *Cereus* by Gürke in 1908 and subsequently transferred to *Arrojadoa* by Britton and Rose. It is a slender, bushy plant with many clustering branches, frequently reaching 2 m (6 ft 6 in) high, or alternatively becoming semi-prostrate with the thin branches at ground level. The branches are rarely much more than 1.5 cm ($\frac{5}{8}$ in) thick, with 10–12 shallow ribs bedecked with closely set areoles; these carry 8–10 short but spreading radial spines and one or two slightly longer centrals. All are needle-like, yellowish to greyish-brown in colour. A

bristly pseudocephalium forms at the top of each stem joint and consists of white wool and brownish bristles; it is from this that the flowers appear. They are usually borne in clusters, often 6 or more to a cluster, each flower being about 2.5 cm (1 in) long and wide. The flowers are deep pink in colour. Fruits are smooth, about 1.5 cm ($\frac{5}{8}$ in) long and purplish. It is one of the most rewarding of the genus, with flowers readily produced year after year.

### A. rhodantha

An equally well-known plant, the specific name rightly indicates its main characteristic, the flower, which is a rich purplish-red. This is the other species included in the original genus of Britton and Rose and native to Brazil (Bahia and Minas Gerais). It has dark green stems, about 2 m (6 ft 6 in) long, and about 4 cm (1$\frac{1}{2}$ in) wide, either clambering or semi-pendent, according to situation. It has about 13 shallow ribs and small areoles set close together which each carry up to 20 brownish radial and 5–6 central spines, all becoming greyish with age. Flowers, each about 3 cm (1$\frac{1}{2}$ in) long and about 1.5 cm ($\frac{5}{8}$ in) across, appear from the pseudocephalium, scarcely protruding beyond the surrounding brown bristles; they are more or less tubular in shape, the petals slightly spreading at the tips. Varieties of the species, such as var. *occibahiensis* and ssp. *reflexa*, vary only in small detail from the type species.

### A. auriespina

Found by Albert F.H. Buining and described by Buining and J.A. Brederoo in 1972, this has a clustering

*Arrojadoa rhodantha*

*Astrophytum asterias*

habit, with stems to about 1 m (3 ft 3 in) long and more than 5 cm (2 in) thick. It has bright yellow spines, and the cephalium is similarly coloured. The flowers are deep pink, about 3 cm (1¼ in) long and only 1 cm (⅜ in) across. It too is from Bahia. Several other new additions include *A. horstii* and *A. multiflora*, and these have many characteristics reminiscent of those already mentioned.

# ASTROPHYTUM

This small but important genus has great attraction for all collectors, beginners and connoisseurs alike. The generic name, which was established by Charles A. Lemaire in 1839, comes from the Greek *astron,* meaning star, and *phyton,* plant. This is clearly obvious with every one of the species, all of which are native to northern parts of Mexico, mostly in calcareous terrain. They appear as globular plants, although the rib formation contributes to a variety of fascinating shapes. They offer but few problems in cultivation and are easily raised from seeds sown early in the year at a temperature of 25°C (77°F). If grown without a rest period for at least one year, quite a sizable plant can develop within two years, by which time the characteristics applying to a particular species become discernible. Provide a rich porous compost, with the addition of lime and well-rotted leaf-mould; water freely throughout the summer months, but let the soil dry out fairly well between waterings; give a weak liquid feed every three of four weeks. Keep the plants in the sunniest position possible, and in winter maintain a temperature of 10°C (50°F), allowing the soil to become reasonably dry.

### A. asterias

This species, from Tamaulipas and Nuevo León in Mexico and from Texas, is the most sought-after species. It was first named in 1845 by Joseph Zuccarini as a species of *Echinocactus*, and Lemaire transferred it to *Astrophytum* in 1868. It is a somewhat flattened, globular plant, to 8 cm (3 in) in diameter, and symmetrically

divided by up to 10 flattened ribs, clearly furrowed with large whitish, spineless areoles spaced in regular rows along the ribs from crown to base. Flowers appear from the crown, bright yellow with a reddish centre and about 3 cm ($1\frac{1}{4}$ in) long and 4 cm ($1\frac{1}{2}$ in) wide when fully open. The fruit is small and berry-like, green and containing a few blackish seeds.

### A. myriostigma

Described by Lemaire in 1839, this is the type species of the genus. It comes from north to central Mexico, on high ground and to altitudes above 2500 m (8200 ft), particularly in San Luis Potosí and Coahuila. It is variable in certain respects; varieties exist denoting particular characteristics – for example, var. *columnare,* which has rather elongated, low-columnar growth, and var. *strongylocarpum,* which has a completely green body and few, if any, woolly patches. The main species is more or less globular or oval, eventually reaching about 20 cm (8 in) high. It is basically green, but so densely covered with whitish dots that the plant takes on a silvery-grey appearance. There are 5 (rarely 8) ribs, deeply furrowed and the edges covered with rows of brownish areoles, but no spines. The flowers, to 6 cm ($2\frac{1}{2}$ in) long and wide, glistening yellow and with a reddish throat, are borne from the crown of the plant. Fruits are berry-like with many shiny, boat-shaped, black seeds.

## A. ornatum

This was given its specific title by Augustin Pyrame de Candolle in 1828, when it was included in *Echinocactus*, but was later confirmed in the present genus by F. Weber. It comes from Hidalgo and Querétaro in Mexico and has a rather cylindrical body, up to 35 cm (14 in) high in maturity, but fairly globular as a younger plant. It has 8 ribs dotted with many areoles, each carrying up to 11 straight, yellowish spines; deeply furrowed, the ribs disclose the silvery-scaly body of the plant. The pale yellow flowers are large, up to 9 cm (3½ in) wide.

## A. capricorne

This cactus from northern Mexico was reclassified by Britton and Rose from *Echinocactus*. It has 7 or 8, sharply defined, slightly twisted ribs with largish areoles set with many long and twisted brown spines up to 5 cm (2 in) long. The body of the plant is closely covered with numerous whitish scales. The sweetly scented flowers are lemon-yellow, about 6 cm (2½ in) long with orange-red throats; stamens, style and stigma lobes are all yellow. The species can be variable, and the differences are botanically recognized.

# AUSTROCACTUS

This small genus of cacti from Patagonia in Argentina was established in 1922 by Britton and Rose. The generic name, from the Latin *australis*, meaning southern, emphasizes the southern aspect of all the species. They are low-growing plants, rarely seen in cultivation, with tuberculate ribs, sometimes developing aerial roots. Flowers are born from the tips of the somewhat dwarfed columnar stems; the floral tube, ovary and fruits are very spiny. They prefer a bright sunny location and a rich porous soil. Water in moderation throughout the growing and flowering periods, never allowing the soil to become too wet. Feed three or four times from June to September, always in dilute form. Kept dry throughout the winter, the plants will accept quite low temperatures during dormancy, down to a minimum of 7°C (45°F). Propagation is from seeds.

## A. bertinii

The type species, from Patagonia, was previously recorded as *Cereus bertinii* by the French cactus grower August Louis Cels in 1863. A. Berger has also included this plant in the genus *Echinocactus*. A somewhat cylindrical stemmed plant to about 40 cm (16 in) tall and 5 cm (2 in) wide, with 10–12 prominent ribs emphasized by tubercles with yellowish, woolly or felted areoles set

Opposite above: *Astrophytum myriostigma*; opposite below: *Astrophytum ornatum*

about 1 cm (⅜ in) apart. The spines consist of about 15 radials, straight and spreading and 1 cm (⅜ in) long, and four slender, hooked brownish centrals 3 cm (1¼ in) in length. The flowers, about 6 cm (2½ in) long, open with many floral segments to spread to 10 cm (4 in) across; they are brownish-red externally, with pinkish-yellow inner petals, the red style protruding well beyond the stamens, which are bright red, like the stigma lobes.

## A. patagonicus

Described by Weber in 1897 as *Cereus patagonicus* and later reclassified as *Malacocarpus* by Britton and Rose, Backeberg made the present transfer. The plant, which is native to Patagonia (Río Negro) in southern Argentina, is semi-columnar, about 50 cm (20 in) tall and 8 cm (3 in) wide, with 9–12 tuberculate ribs. Areoles carry about 16 whitish-brown radial spines, 2 cm (¾ in) long, and one to four central spines, approximately 4 cm (1½ in) long. Pinkish-white flowers are about 4 cm (1½ in) long and slightly wider when fully expanded. The thick violet style and almost black-purple stigma lobes are outstanding features.

# AUSTROCEPHALOCEREUS

A small genus, which was created by Backeberg in 1937 to contain a few tall-growing, columnar plants that, in maturity, develop elongated cephaliums. The genera *Espostoopsis* and *Gerocephalus* are considered synonymous. The name, from the Latin *australis* meaning southern, and the Greek *kephale*, meaning head, describes the attractive cephalium which forms on the upper sides of mature stems. The species are native to Brazil and possibly Bolivia. The plants have numerous ribs, with many radial and only few central spines. Flowers, which are nocturnal, are borne laterally from the cephalium; they are somewhat tubular in shape, with a scaleless, smooth floral tube, and are followed by large, shapely pink or purplish fruits. In general, they are reasonably quick-growing plants, requiring a warm, sunny position and a porous cactus compost with limestone chippings added. Water moderately from April to October, letting the soil dry out between each watering; add a weak liquid fertilizer to the water every 3–4 weeks. Keep the compost dry in winter, although an occasional overhead spray is beneficial; maintain a minimum temperature of 13°C (55°F). Propagation is by cuttings in summer, or by seeds in late winter and early spring.

## A. purpureus

The type species, selected by Backeberg, was previously known as *Cephalocereus purpureus*, and it is native to Bahia, Brazil, where it grows at altitudes of about 1000 m (3200 ft). It is a tall, usually unbranched,

*Austrocephalocereus dybowskii*

columnar plant to more than 3 m (10 ft) tall and 12 cm (4½ in) thick, with 12–15 broad, low-set ribs with areoles set about 6 mm (¼ in) apart, a V-shaped, white woolly notch over each. The white radial spines, 20 or more in number, are 1 cm (⅜ in) long, while the 4–10 brownish central spines are about 5 cm (2 in) in length. In habitat, and probably in cultivation, the cephalium forms on the west-facing side of mature stems; it can be up to 1 m (3 ft 3 in) long, greyish-white and woolly with blackish-brown bristles. The nocturnal flowers, to 5 cm (2 in) long, have pinkish tubes and outer segments, white inner petals and yellowish style and stigma lobes.

### A. dybowskii
Described by R. Gosselin, a French botanist, in 1908, this was included in *Espostoopsis* before being transferred to the present genus by Franz Buxbaum. From Bahia in Brazil, it branches from the base, with stems to 4 m (13 ft) high and many ribs almost obliterated by the long white hairs and wool of the areoles. The cephalium, massed in woolly hairs and bearing white, bell-shaped flowers to 6 cm (2½ in) long, can reach 60 cm (2 ft).

# AZTEKIUM

This unusual genus was named by F. Boedeker in 1929 because the colour of the rock-like body and the lateral, very distinctive ribs are said to be reminiscent of original designs in the sculptures of the early Aztek Indians. It is found only on the dry stone slopes in Nuevo León in Mexico where it is scarcely discernible in the similarly coloured rocky terrain. Some authorities suggest that this is by no means an easy plant in cultivation, but, while it is quite uncommon and probably best termed a connoisseur's plant, if it receives careful and precise attention it will succeed in growth and flower. It needs full sun, an open, very porous gritty compost and a totally dry rest period in winter, at a temperature of 70°C (45°F). Propagation is by seed.

### A. ritteri
The type species, named by Boedeker in tribute to Friedrich Ritter, a collector and widely respected authority on the Cactaceae, has stems that are more or less globular, depressed or somewhat flattened on the top, greyish-green in colour and rarely exceeding 2–3 cm (¾–1¼ in) high and 5–6 cm (2–2½ in) thick. Offsets often develop from the base to form closely set, small clumps. There are 9–11 ribs, about 1 cm (⅜ in) high and 8 mm (¼ in) wide, forming deep furrows; the areoles are minute, white and hairy and set closely together along the ribs. Thin, papery white spines, 1–4 in number, about 4 mm (⅛ in) long, usually drop off as the plants mature. Pinkish-white flowers appear in the crown of the plant, developing from the new areoles; they are wide open, rather funnel-shaped and about 1 cm (⅜ in) long and 8 mm (¼ in) wide; the stigma is yellowish with 4 lobes. The fruits are small and pink.

*Aztekium ritteri*

# BERGEROCACTUS

A monotypic genus, raised by Britton and Rose in 1909 to honour Alwin Berger, for many years the curator at the garden of Sir Thomas Hanbury at La Mortola in Italy and an authority on Cactaceae. These many-branched plants have a particular attraction with their almost rambling growth of golden-spined stems and branches and with flowers appearing in clusters at the tips. The closest allies are *Pachycereus* and *Stenocereus*, with which they share the habitat of southerly parts of California and the Baja (Lower) California of Mexico. A really bright and sunny position is essential if the plants are to look their best; sun also helps to display the bright colouring of the spines to advantage. A proprietary cactus compost is suitable, with added gritty sand for improved drainage. Water thoroughly during the growing season of spring and summer, with fertilizer every four weeks, then gradually reduce watering, until the plants are dry for the winter dormancy. Keep at a minimum temperature of about 10°C (50°F). Propagation is from cuttings or seeds.

### B. emoryi

Initially described by G. Engelmann as *Cereus emoryi* and in 1885 by Theodor Rümpler as *Echinocereus emoryi*, it has now been transferred as type species of *Bergerocactus*. It branches to about 60 cm (2 ft) long with 20–25 low ribs and areoles carrying up to 30 bright yellow or brownish-yellow radial spines, about 2 cm ($\frac{3}{4}$ in) long, and one to three centrals to 4 cm ($1\frac{1}{2}$ in); they appear very densely set because the areoles are barely 1 cm ($\frac{3}{8}$ in) apart. The bright yellow flowers are funnel-shaped, about 2 cm ($\frac{3}{4}$ in) or more long and about the same wide when fully expanded; the tube is short and covered with minute scales. Fruits are more or less round, about 3 cm ($1\frac{1}{4}$ in) wide and very spiny.

# BLOSSFELDIA

A very small genus of more or less miniature cacti, all known species being native to Argentina and Bolivia. It was established in 1927 by E. Werdermann and named in honour of the discoverer of the first species, *Blossfeldia liliputana,* Harry Blossfeld Jr, whose expeditions to Brazil and other South American countries have resulted in many finds of horticultural interest. All species are extremely small, in fact the tiniest plants within Cactaceae. The rounded stems lack ribs and are entirely without spines. Flowers, too, are short and appear from or near the crown. In general, they are mountain plants growing among rocks and stones. They are not considered too easy in cultivation, and much care is needed to establish them on their own roots. They are better grafted as seedlings on to a small but vigorous stock that will encourage excellent growth; they may then form quite compact clusters and, eventually, flower. They can be raised successfully from the minute, almost dust-like seeds; the process of germination is slow, and growth thereafter is hardly discernible for several years, unless the seedlings are grafted after about three years, preferable on root stock of *Trichocereus* or *Echinopsis*. The compost should contain loam and leaf-mould with fine gritty

*Bergerocactus emoryi*

sand added to ensure good drainage. Temperatures should not be allowed to fall below 13°C (55°F) whether the plants are on their own roots or grafted; always provide a very bright site.

### B. liliputana

The type species is native to north Argentina (Jujuy) and Bolivia (Tarija). It is a small flattish circular plant with greyish-green body, up to 1 cm ($\frac{3}{8}$ in) in diameter, covered with minute greyish woolly areoles and totally without spines. The pinkish-white flowers, about 1 cm ($\frac{3}{8}$ in) across, appear from near the crown, at any time from spring until autumn. The plant is said to cluster reasonably well on its own roots, and will certainly do so if grafted.

### B. minima

Very similar to the above, *B. minima* may well prove to be a form of it. It was described by Friedrich Ritter, who recorded its habitat as Potosí in Bolivia. The body is only to 6 mm ($\frac{1}{4}$ in) wide, otherwise identical to *B. liliputana*.

Two other species are recorded, but they vary only slightly from those mentioned.

# BORZICACTUS

This somewhat controversial genus was established in 1909 by V. Riccobono, and it honours Antonio Borzi from the Botanical Gardens in Palermo, Italy. It was originally established for a single species, *B. ventimigliae*, which has since become a synonym of *B. sepium*. Several species have been added over the years, and more recently several genera, including *Akersia, Clistanthocereus, Hildewintera, Loxanthocereus* and others, have become absorbed into *Borzicactus*. There is now every likelihood that the whole genus will become merged with *Cleistocactus*, although this may mean further complications as new species that might well fall into the category of *Borzicactus* are discovered. Here, those species which are diurnal and have relatively zygomorphic flowers are considered as belonging to *Borzicactus,* and this may well involve more than 50 species. They are all columnar plants, generally of somewhat bushy habit, and bear reddish flowers. They are mainly from mountainous and hilly parts of Ecuador, Peru and Bolivia, probably also Chile. Without exception, they can be cultivated very successfully, provided that they are given a bright sunny position; shaded conditions can prove detrimental to good flowering. Use any proprietary cactus compost, always ensuring that the mixture is porous; if in doubt add more gritty sand. Regular watering from April to October is important, with fertilizer added every 3–4 weeks to help invigorate growth and encourage flowering. During the period from November to March, maintain a minimum temperature of about 10°C (50°F) and keep the compost dry; if the temperature exceeds the minimum, water carefully so as to prevent the roots from drying out completely. Propagation is from cuttings taken in early summer or by seeds sown between January and March, in a compost similar to that for established plants.

## B. sepium

Originally described as *Cactus sepium* by Humboldt, Bonpland and Kunth, Britton and Rose incorporated it in

*Blossfeldia liliputana*

*Borzicactus* in 1920. The type species, *B. ventimigliae*, appears to be totally synonymous. The plant is columnar, either erect or semi-prostrate, stems being 1.5 m (5 ft) tall and about 4 cm (1½ in) thick with 8–11 notched ribs. Areoles are set about 2 cm (¾ in) apart and bear 8–10 thin radial spines, about 1 cm (⅜ in) long, and one or two downward-pointing centrals 2–4 cm (¾–1½ in) in length; all spines are yellowish-red but turn grey with age. The somewhat zygomorphic flowers, about 4 cm (1½ in) long, are bright scarlet. The variety *B. sepium* var. *morleyanus* which once enjoyed specific status, is from Ecuador, like the type. The stems are generally thicker, to 6 cm (2½ in) and are more likely to spread into clumps. Ribs number 13–16, with areoles bearing 15–18 or more radial spines. Flowers, to 6 cm (2½ in) long, are red with a prominent, cream-coloured style.

## B. samaipatanus

Described by the Bolivian botanist Cardenas, it comes from the Santa Cruz area of Bolivia and is probably one of the finest of the genus as far as exotic flowering is concerned. Stems are up to 1.5 m (5 ft) long and about 5 cm (2 in) thick, and branching freely. There are 13–16 ribs with areoles bearing 30–40 bright yellow, slender spines 1–4 cm (⅜–1½ in) long. The flowers are vivid bright red and the petals are lightly suffused lilac at the edges.

### B. aureispinus

Found in Florida in Bolivia, *B. aureispinus* was previously described by Ritter as *Hildewintera* in 1966, and was transferred to *Borzicactus* in 1973 by Gordon Rowley. It is of slightly sprawling and trailing habit, with stems that are bright green and about 1.5 m (5 ft) long and 2.5 cm (1 in) or a little more thick. There are about 16 ribs, with brownish areoles bearing numerous soft, golden-yellow spines, about 1 cm ($\frac{3}{8}$ in) long. Flowers are borne along the length of the stems; they are about 5 cm (2 in) long and wide, the inner petals yellowish-red, the outer flower segments orange and deeper red.

### B. aurivillus

A native of northern Peru, this was initially named as *Cereus aurivillus* by K. Schumann and transferred to the current genus by Britton and Rose in 1923. A clustering species with stems to 25 cm (10 in) long and 2.5 cm (1 in) thick, almost cylindrical in shape. Ribs number about 17, and they are notched with closely set areoles of yellow wool bearing 30 or more pale yellowish spines. Flowers,

*Borzicactus samaipatanus*

several together, appear from the tips of the stems; they are about 6 cm ($2\frac{1}{2}$ in) long, carmine red and with bristly tufts at the base.

Many introductions by Ritter and Backeberg have added considerable significance to this genus: the reddish colouring of the flowers is apparent with all species and strikingly evident with *B. samnensis* and *B. sextonianus*, previously recorded as *Loxanthocereus*. The species *B. roseiflorus*, the erstwhile solitary member of the now obsolete genus *Akersia*, is of semi-erect, sprawling habit; it is distinguished with many golden yellow spines and pale red flowers about 5 cm (2 in) long.

# BRACHYCEREUS

In 1920 Britton and Rose established this genus for a single species. It takes its name from the Greek *brachys*, meaning short, which refers to the plant's fairly low-growing stature. Some confusion surrounds this one species. It has, as *Cereus thouarsii*, been referred to *Jasminocereus* and is, indeed, similar to, or synonymous with, *J. galapagensis*. There was also *Cereus nesioticus*, thought for a while to be synonymous with *Cereus thouarsii*, which had by then become the sole species within *Brachycereus*. Subsequently, it was decided that the two were different, and now the solitary species is *Brachycereus nesioticus*. It comes from the Galapagos Islands and is fairly widespread in all the islands. It is uncommon in cultivation, but can be grown to perfection if provided with a truly bright and sunny position and a minimum temperature of 16°C (60°F) at all times. The compost must be enriched with humus and made porous with plenty of sharp gritty sand added. Water in moderation at all times, and in winter only sufficiently to prevent the soil from drying out completely. Feed with a weak liquid fertilizer every 3–4 weeks from May to September. Propagation is by cuttings or seeds.

### *B. nesioticus*

This clump-forming, columnar plant was earlier known as *Cereus nesioticus*. The erect stems, about 60 cm (2 ft) long, have 13–16 shallow ribs with areoles set fairly closely, each about 2 mm ($\frac{1}{16}$ in). Spines are numerous, usually 30 or more, to about 3 cm ($1\frac{1}{4}$ in) long. The white nocturnal flowers are about 7 cm ($2\frac{3}{4}$ in) long and 2.5 cm (1 in) across; the tube is spiny and scaly. Fruits are reddish-brown, about 2.5 cm (1 in) long and 1.5 cm ($\frac{5}{8}$ in) wide. This still remains a poorly understood plant; it has many similarities to species of *Haageocereus* and might well belong to that genus.

# BROWNINGIA

This is generally considered a genus with very few close allies. Raised by Britton and Rose in 1920, it was originally monotypic, but currently includes about seven species, largely because *Azureocereus* and *Gymnocereus* were united under the one generic name. It was named in honour of W.E. Browning, an American botanist working in Chile. All species are native to Chile and Peru and are tall, tree-like plants, branching principally from the top of erect trunks. There are numerous low-set ribs, many-spined, especially on the main trunk or stem. Nocturnal flowers are borne singly from areoles on the upper part of the branches; an outstanding feature is the floral tube, which is covered with large thin, slightly fleshy scales. By no means difficult in cultivation, plants require a good sunny position, a rich compost and moderate watering from May to October and during dormancy, at a winter temperature of 10°C (50°F). Feed at 3–4 week intervals from June to September. Propagation is by seeds.

### *B. candelaris*

The type species was originally described by F.J.F. Meyen as *Cereus candelaris* in 1883. It is a desert plant, from altitudes of about 2500 m (8200 ft). In the wild, it can attain 5 m ($16\frac{1}{2}$ ft) in height, with a trunk about 30 cm (1 ft) in diameter, bright-green in colour with long spines, more so when young. The main stem gradually tapers towards the top and only from here are somewhat drooping branches produced. There are 30–34 ribs, with rounded areoles bearing yellow-brown radial and central spines in varying numbers and lengths according to the age of the plant, often 10 cm (4 in) long. The flowers are 12 cm ($4\frac{1}{2}$ in) long; the scaly tube is slightly curved, the outer petals are brown, the inner ones white or pinkish, and stamens, style and stigma lobes are creamy white.

### *B. hertlingiana*

Included in *Azureocereus* by Backeberg, then placed in *Browningia* by Buxbaum, it comes from the Mantaro Valley in Peru and is a truly beautiful species, with bluish-green, erect stems that, in the wild, can reach 8 m (26 ft 6 in) high with a girth of about 30 cm (1 ft). The 18 or more ribs are set with regularly spaced areoles and yellowish-brown radial and central spines, varying in number; the latter can be up to 8 cm (3 in) long, depending on the age of the plant. The flowers are white.

# BUININGIA

A small genus named in 1971 by Franz Buxbaum in honour of A.F.H. Buining, the Dutch botanist. All three species are native to the Minas Gerais region of Brazil. They are globular to short-cylindrical plants with up to 18 ribs, producing a cephalium when they have reached maturity. The genus is closely allied to *Coleocephalocereus*, but differs in flower structure and the seeds, which are not dissimilar to those of *Melocactus*. Whether this merits segregation remains a taxonomic problem still to be resolved. These plants are some of the most sought-after, rare cactus species and, with due care, they present no great difficulties in cultivation. A sunny position is essential, both summer and winter. Winter temperatures are best kept at a minimum of 10° (50°F), higher if possible. A rich mineral soil is advisable; the need to include ample sharp sand cannot be over-emphasized. If a normal cactus compost is used, add more grit to ensure the mix is really porous. Water regularly throughout the late spring and summer months; if a higher temperature than the minimum is maintained in winter, give an occasional watering to prevent the rootstock drying out. Propagation is from seeds sown January to March, at a temperature of 22°C (72°F) or slightly more; the compost should be kept moist and shaded from direct sun until germination has taken place.

*Buiningia aurea*

## B. brevicylindrica

Initially placed in *Coleocephalocereus* by Buining, but later transferred to the current genus by Buxbaum, this has a short cylindrical stem, about 30 cm (12 in) tall and 15–17 cm (6–6¾ in) thick at the base. Ribs number about 17, with areoles bearing 7 radial spines from 1.5–3 cm (⅝–1¼ in) long and about four longer centrals. The cephalium (or pseudocephalium) develops on one side of the stem near the top and consists of numerous bristle-like spines of bright orange-yellow which appear through a dense mass of whitish wool becoming black with age. Flowers, yellowish-green in colour and somewhat tubular in shape, protrude through the cephalium; they are approximately 3 cm (1¼ in) long and 1.5 cm (⅝ in) wide.

## B. aurea

Very similar to the above, but tends to develop offsets quite freely from the base so that small colonies are formed. The yellowish flowers are followed by berry-like red fruits.

# CALYMMANTHIUM

A genus of only two species, which was established by F. Ritter in 1926, the name comes from the Greek *kalumma*, meaning veiled, and *anthos*, meaning flower. This adequately describes the outstanding feature of these species, a flower bud resembling a new shoot; the nocturnal flower eventually protrudes through the tip. These columnar plants, which are native to Peru, often attain tree-like proportions or form thick clumps, 5–8 m (16 ft 6 in–26 ft 6 in) high; they have but few ribs and spines. In cultivation, the plants require a bright sunny position and a rich compost containing loam, leaf-mould and sharp sand, with limestone chippings added; water moderately throughout the growing and flowering seasons and give an occasional feed during these periods. Keep the plants dry in winter, at a minimum temperature of 10°C (50°F). Propagation is from seeds sown early in the year.

*Calymmanthium substerile*

### C. substerile

This tree-like plant from Jaén in Peru grows to more than 8 m (26 ft 6 in) tall in its wild habitat with branches 1 m (3 ft 3 in) long and 8 cm (3 in) thick. Three or four very narrow ribs are set with whitish areoles bearing 3–8 radial spines, 1 cm ($\frac{3}{8}$ in) long, and about 6 centrals to 5 cm (2 in) long in length, all white in colour. The flowers, 11 cm ($4\frac{1}{4}$ in), are reddish-brown externally, white inside.

### C. fertile

A native of high ground, east of Balsas, Peru, this species grows to about 6 m (20 ft) tall with branches 4–8 cm ($1\frac{1}{2}$–3 in) thick. The 4 ribs have orange-felted areoles bearing many horn-coloured spines. Flowers are about 8 cm (3 in) long, sometimes longer, with brown outer petals and dark yellowish-white inner petals.

# CARNEGIEA

This is a unique genus, created by Britton and Rose in 1909. The solitary species had previously been known under different names and even today there is evidence that such genera as *Neodawsonia, Neobuxbaumia* and *Rooksbya* could be united with *Carnegiea* – a develop-
ment that may well occur in the near future. *Carnegiea* is the giant cactus of the Arizona and Sonora deserts and also occurs in the south of California. The generic name honours the Scottish-born philanthropist, Andrew Carnegie, who was a patron of the arts and sciences. The specific name is self-explanatory, denoting the outstanding size and dimensions; the species is commonly known as saguaro or the sahuaro, its huge tree-like form providing a magnificent silhouette at sunset in the desert. It is a columnar plant with a dark-green trunk and thick, semi-erect branches, likely in old age to attain 14 m (46 ft) in height and more than 60 cm (2 ft) in width; birds brave the heavy spines to bore nest holes in the trunk. It is a slow grower, particularly in the early stages; it can take up to 40 years to reach 1 m (3 ft 3 in) or a little more in height. Once it achieves this size, however, growth becomes more rapid, especially in its natural habitat. Grow in a proprietary cactus compost, with added gritty sand to improve drainage. Keep in a bright sunny position, water moderately during the summer months and feed every 3–4 weeks during the growing period, which is certain to encourage quicker development. They grow readily from seeds sown in any good commercially branded seed compost; maintain a temperature of 21°C (70°F) until germination is assured, then keep at about 15°C (60°F) until growth reaches approximately 2 cm ($\frac{3}{4}$ in), when seedlings can be more or less treated as normal

Opposite and above: *Carnegiea gigantea*; right:
*Cephalocereus senilis*

plants, although progress will be very slow. Keep the plants fairly dry in winter, at a minimum temperature of 7°C (45°F).

### C. gigantea

Previously known as *Cereus giganteus*, it may have several branches, but not until many years have passed. The plant body has 12–24 ribs bearing brown woolly areoles, each with 12 or more stiff brownish radial spines, about 2 cm ($\frac{3}{4}$ in) long, and 3–6 thicker central spines to 8 cm (3 in) long. Flowers occur on mature plants only; they are situated right at the top of the plant where the areoles, which bear the flowers, have many extremely long and sharp spines. The trumpet-shaped flowers themselves are about 12 cm ($4\frac{1}{2}$ in) long and wide, the sepals greenish-white, the petals pure white and stamens and style creamy-white, with about 15 stigma lobes. Flowers tend to open at night, but they last through well into the following afternoon. The red fruit, which is in the form of a large berry, is approximately 9 cm ($3\frac{1}{2}$ in) long and is said to be edible.

# CEPHALOCEREUS

This genus at one time included nearly 50 species from both northern and southern countries of America, but with reclassification it can boast of just one. The generic name, provided by Ludwig Pfeiffer in 1838, is from the Greek *kephale*, meaning head, and applies to the woolly and spiny crown or pseudocephalium that develops at the tops of the stems when they reach maturity. These columnar cacti grow very tall in their natural habitat, often to 10 m (33 ft) in height, and they produce flowers

only after the development of the pseudocephalium, from which they emerge. They are by no means difficult in cultivation, their white hairy appearance being apparent from seedling stage. Plants require a very light, preferably sunny position and a temperature never below 15°C (59°F). Careful watering is essential; overwatering can prove disastrous. For best results, grow in a commercially produced cactus compost, with additional sharp sand and limestone chippings; this not only ensures good drainage, but also helps to enhance the attraction of the white hairs. Plants can be grown from seeds sown during January to March, at a temperature of 21°C (70°F) or more; keep the compost just moist and shaded from the sun until after germination, then gradually expose the seedlings to more light. They can be pricked out individually when they are about 2.5 cm (1 in) high.

### C. senilis

The old-man cactus, which has gained much popularity, was one of the earliest cacti described. It was listed by A.H. Haworth as *Cactus senilis* in 1824. It is usually solitary, rarely producing branches and then only if the stem is damaged. It has numerous ribs, 12–15 on young plants, but more than double these numbers when plants are mature. The spines are long, bristly and hairy, with 20–30 radials more than 10 cm (4 in) long, and 1–5 shorter centrals varying in length as the plants grow taller. The pseudocephalium is rarely one-sided, and becomes evident when plants are 5 m (16 ft 6 in) or more tall; it gradually covers the whole top surface of the plant with dense, white and bristly hairs and wool. Flowers can then emerge; they are nocturnal, creamy-white or yellowish on the inner surface of the petals, red outside, up to nearly 10 cm (4 in) long and 7 cm (2¾ in) across.

# CEREUS

At one time all columnar cactus species were included in this genus, and the name is still often wrongly used when referring to certain species of tall-growing plants. The name *Cereus* goes back to Philip Miller, the English plantsman, who officially established the genus in 1754, at the same time giving credit to P. Hermann, who is recorded as having proposed this title in 1698. The name is from both the Greek and Latin *cereus*, meaning torch or candle, and relates to the particular candelabra-like growth of many of the earliest species described.

The genus now comprises some 50 species from various parts of South America and the West Indies. Many tall-growing plants are included but seemingly only those in which the number of ribs is restricted to 8–10. Many well-known species are encompassed, and with but few exceptions they are of easy growth and are rela-

tively easy to obtain. Some of the species, as young plants, have proved exceedingly useful as grafting stock for less vigorous cacti.

In cultivation, a good porous cactus compost will give excellent results. Water freely during the growing season, with a fertilizer added every 4–6 weeks; during the winter months, if the temperature is kept at a minimum of 10°C (50°F), it is advisable to give sufficient water to prevent the roots drying out completely. Propagation can be by cuttings in summer, or by seeds sown January to March, at a temperature of 21°C (70°F), using a proprietary seed compost. The seeds should be just covered, not buried, and the compost kept moist and shaded from full sun until the seeds have germinated and good sturdy growth is obvious. It is best not to prick out the seedlings individually until they are 4–5 cm (1½–2 in) high.

### C. peruvianus

One of the very earliest cactus species on record, it was named *Cactus peruvianus* by Linnaeus in 1753. It was placed in *Cereus* in 1768, and there it has remained ever since. Just where this plant originates is still uncertain, certainly not Peru where no plant of this description exists, and it is more likely to have come from Brazil or Argentina, where it still abounds in plenty. A tree-like

*Cereus chalybaeus*

plant, growing to well over 4 m (13 ft) high in congenial surroundings, with stems 20 cm (8 in) or more thick on larger specimens. The stems are pale bluish-green becoming a duller green, with up to eight, slightly notched ribs; brownish areoles appear at each notch. These carry about seven straight radial spines and one or two centrals, all brownish, varying in size from 1 to 2 cm ($\frac{3}{8}$–$\frac{3}{4}$ in) long. The nocturnal flowers are very large – up to 16 cm ($6\frac{1}{4}$ in) long – with pure white inner petals, tinged pink outside. A number of exceedingly attractive cristate or monstrous forms are known, and these thrive as readily as the type species but are more loath to flower.

### C. chalybaeus

This comes from Uruguay and Argentina and was described by Christoph Otto in 1846. The stems, which rarely exceed 2–3 m (6 ft 6 in–10 ft) in height in the wild, and certainly not in cultivation, are a beautiful bluish-green and have 5–6 ribs . Plants can become tree-like with a few branches from towards the base. The spines are an outstanding feature; the 7–9 radials are brown with black tips, the centrals invariably black and glistening, and both types to about 1.5 cm ($\frac{5}{8}$ in) long. The flowers are about 20 cm (8 in) long, with white, slightly toothed inner petals and fairly reddish outer petals.

Several other species are very similar in habit and growth, differing only in small details. *C. aethiops*, from Argentina and Brazil, is known for its purplish-green stems, black areoles and black spines. *C. jamacaru* from Bahia, Brazil, is frequently encountered in cultivation. It grows to 10 m (33 ft), is bright-green in colour and has few ribs, many yellow spines and large white flowers, sometimes up to 30 cm (1 ft) long.

# CLEISTOCACTUS

This genus was established by Charles A. Lemaire in 1861 for a comparatively small number of species. The name is from the Greek word *cleistos*, meaning closed, and refers to the long unexpanding tubular flower, which remains more or less closed except for the tips of the petals. It is one of several genera with similar characteristics, including *Borzicactus,* which with a number of other well-known names, might eventually be brought together under this generic heading. They are slender columnar plants, erect or semi-erect in habit, generally branching from the base and frequently 2 m (6 ft 6 in) or more in length. The species all grow in a number of South American countries, principally at altitudes from 500 m (approximately 1650 ft) to more than 3000 m (approximately 10,000 ft). The majority have quite dense, colourful spination, and the nocturnal flowers appear towards

*Cleistocactus* aff. *baumannii*

the upper part of the branches, usually projecting laterally. In cultivation they are best given a really sunny position and provided with a rich compost, to which humus can be added to advantage. Those described here from higher altitudes should be allowed a period of dry dormancy in winter (minimum temperature 10°C (50°F)), but with frequent watering during the rest of the year. Other species, mainly those from lower altitudes, are best given a higher temperature in winter, about 15°C (60°F) or more, and watered throughout the year, just sufficiently to prevent the soil from drying out. Propagation is by cuttings in summer or seeds sown early in the year.

### C. strausii

The best known of this group, it was named *Cereus strausii* by the German authority E. Heese in 1907, subsequently being reclassified under the present title by Backeberg. It is from Bolivia (Tarija), where it almost dominates the hillsides. Stems are straight and slender, to 1 m (3 ft 3 in) or more tall, generally branching from or near the base. They have 25 or more narrow ribs covered with pure white, bristly hairs and set with areoles each bearing 30 or more white radials and 3–5 pale yellow central spines. The flowers stand out straight from the

*Cleistocactus ritteri*

stems; they are 8–9 cm (3–3½ in) long, deep carmine-red and hairy along the length of the flower tube. The petals open only at the very tip to expose the reddish stamens and yellow style.

### C. baumannii

One of the first species of the genus to be recorded by Lemaire, it is from quite high ground in Uruguay, Paraguay and Argentina and is generally an erect plant about 1 m (3 ft 3 in) high, very stiff and only about 4 cm (1½ in) thick. There are about 14 ribs with brownish areoles carrying numerous brownish spines, some 4 cm (1½ in) or more long. The flowers are bright scarlet, although sometimes they have a tinge of orange, each approximately 7 cm (2¾ in) long and often slightly curved.

### C. ritteri

Previously known as *Cephalocleistocactus*, Backeberg provided the original description. It was discovered in Yungas, Bolivia. A plant from hilly country, it has up-

right stems and 14–16 ribs, which are heavily spined, particularly in the area of flowering where the areoles produce numerous white bristles about 4 cm (1½ in) long. The flowers, about 4 cm (1½ in) in length, are greenish-yellow in colour and are inclined to point slightly downwards.

### C. brookei

Probably the rarest species, it was first described by M. Cardenas as *Cleistocactus wendlandiorum*. A noble Bolivian species, the erect or semi-erect stems are more than 1 m (3 ft 3 in) long and 5 cm (2 in) or more in diameter; brown areoles are set at close intervals along the 20–25 ribs, each areole bearing numerous white bristly spines, which appear particularly at the tips of the stems. The tubular flowers, which are a bright orange-red, are approximately 5 cm (2 in) long, scarcely opening at the tips. The flowers tend to stand semi-erect near the tops of the stems.

# COLEOCEPHALOCEREUS

A rather small genus of South American plants, closely linked to *Cephalocereus*, but separated because of the naked, funnel-shaped flowers, a feature that also segregates it from *Buiningia* with which it has a close affinity. There are possibly 7 species, all bearing a cephalium from which the nocturnal flowers emerge. The generic name, given by Curt Backeberg in 1938, is from the Greek *koleos*, sheath, and *kephale*, head, a reference to the sheathed head or cephalium evident in all species. The stems are columnar, up to 1.5 m (5 ft) high, erect or semi-erect to almost prostrate. Flowers always develop once the cephalium has formed and protrude through the wool and bristles. These are by no means common plants, although the type species is one of the very earliest known cacti, while others are among more recent discoveries. All species need a well-lit, sunny position and a well-draining proprietary cactus compost with added limestone chippings to simulate their natural calcareous surroundings. Careful watering is essential; too much can lead to rotting. Keep the plants fairly dry in winter at a temperature of 10°C (50°F). Propagate from cuttings taken in the late summer or by seeds sown at a high temperature during the months of January to March.

### C. fluminensis

The type species has, seemingly, been difficult to classify ever since its first mention by J.M. da C. Vellozo in 1825 under the name *Cactus melocactus,* later being renamed as *Cereus fluminensis* by the Dutch botanist F.A.W. Miquel in 1838. Other synonyms relate to this plant, all in other genera, such as *Cephalocereus* and *Pilocereus*. It is from the rocky cliff faces near the coastline in Rio de Janeiro, Brazil, a sprawling, clambering plant with stems up to 1 m (3 ft 3 in) or more in length and branching freely to form clumps. There are 10–17 broad, rounded ribs with white woolly areoles bearing yellowish spines made up of 4–7 radial and one central, all about 3 cm (1¼ in) long. The cephalium forms on one side of the stems, about 5 cm (2 in) wide and 60 cm (2 ft) or more long, consisting of dense white wool and yellow bristles. The flowers are about 6 cm (2½ in) long, the outer flower segments pinkish, the shorter inner petals white with a very long white style protruding beyond both stamens and petals. The fruit is a smooth purplish berry, about 3 cm (1¼ in) long.

### C. goebelianus

Named by Backeberg following F. Vaupel's earlier description, this is endemic to Bahia and Minas Gerais in Brazil. It has also been known as *Cephalocereus purpureus*. It is a tall erect plant, which in the wild can reach to 5 m (16 ft 6 in) and 12 cm (4½ in) across. There are about 25 prominent ribs, closely notched with supporting areoles along the edges, each with up to 25 radial spines, about 1.5 cm (⅝ in) long, and a few spreading centrals to 5 cm (2 in) in length, all brownish-yellow and frequently curved. The cephalium occurs on one side of the stems, from which appear whitish-pink flowers approximately 3–4 cm (1¼–1½ in) long; the fruits are purplish in colour.

### C. pluricostatus

One of the more recent introductions, this was discovered in Minas Gerais, Brazil, and named and described by Buining and Backeberg. A clump-forming species with stems more than 3 m (10 ft) long and 9 cm (3½ in) thick, with more than 20 close-set, rather acute ribs, bearing areoles with about five radials and one central spine no more than 1 cm (⅜ in) long. The woolly cephalium has a mass of brownish-yellow or black bristly spines; from these appear the white flowers, which are only about 2.5 cm (1 in) long.

Other discoveries have been recorded following the plant expeditions of Friedrich Ritter. They include *C. paulensis*, also a sprawling plant, and the smaller growing *C. decumbens*, both from Brazil.

# COPIAPOA

A genus of interesting globular cacti from Chile. The generic name comes from Copiapó, one of the regions of that country, and all species inhabit coastal areas. A number of the species now included were previously listed in *Echinocactus* before 1922 when Britton and Rose proposed this separate grouping. It is difficult to determine just how many species are contained within the genus. It depends mainly upon which authority is accepted – there is still confusion. They are almost conical in shape and distinctive with their chalky-white stems; a few have brownish colouring. Most species are a little difficult to grow and require a rather semi-shaded position. A relatively open compost is important, especially for those species having taproots. Very careful watering is essential for success; generally the growing season starts in mid-summer and carries through until October. Give a complete rest from November until late March at a temperature down to 7°C (45°F). Plants can be successfully grown from seeds, but no flowers can be expected for at least three years.

### C. cinerea

Formerly referred to *Echinocactus* by R.A. Philippi in 1860 but brought into the current genus in 1922, this is the largest species. In its natural habitat of Antofagasta, west Chile, it is more or less cylindrical, eventually be-

*Copiapoa cinerea*

coming elongated to more than 1 m (3 ft 3 in) and about 20 cm (8 in) in width and frequently offsetting to form groups. It has fibrous roots with a chalky-greyish body with a densely woolly crown, and 18–25 broad and rounded ribs with closely set areoles. Spines are black, at first up to 6 in number, later only one or three. The yellow flowers are 2.5 cm (1 in) long, with yellow stamens. Fruits are about 2 cm ($\frac{3}{4}$ in) long, pinkish-yellow and contain glossy black seeds.

### C. hypogaea

A native of Atacama and Antofagasta, Chile, this globular, brownish-green plant is about 6 cm (2$\frac{1}{2}$ in) wide and woolly-tufted in the crown and has about 14 spirally arranged ribs divided into shallow tubercles. Small, whitish areoles bear about 8 spines, which are whitish at the base and brownish-black towards the tips; they usually fall off after a short while. The broadly funnel-shaped, yellowish flowers are borne during summer and autumn. The species grows from a thick taproot. The form var. *barquitensis*, also described by Ritter, differs but little from the type.

# CORRYOCACTUS

This genus of some 40 or more species, established in 1920 by Britton and Rose, originally included just three species. It was named after a Peruvian engineer, T.A. Corry, who aided early-day plant explorers with their expeditions. All are columnar, some attaining heights of 3 m (10 ft) or more, branching primarily near the base so as to form quite thick, bushy plants. Recent research has resulted in the genus *Erdisia* being merged with *Corryocactus*, and there seems every justification for

this combination. Plants are generally considered easy to grow but rather difficult to flower, although flowers can be achieved when plants reach true maturity. All are high-mountain plants, native to Bolivia, Peru and Chile, centred to no small degree at different altitudes of the Andes to more than 3500 m (11,000 ft). Plants require a really porous, calcareous soil, a bright and sunny position, moderate watering during the warmest months and to be kept fairly dry throughout winter. They withstand quite low temperatures during dormancy as long as the soil is not wet, or even moist, but for safety a minimum of 7°C (45°F) is advisable. Propagation is best by cuttings taken in summer. Insert the cuttings in an open, sandy compost and kept shaded from full sun until rooting is assured.

### C. brevistylus

Previously known as *Cereus brevistylus*, so named by Karl Schumann, this became the type species of *Corryocactus* when Britton and Rose established it in 1920. It is native to northern parts of Chile and southern regions of Peru. The stems are erect, 2–3 m (6–10 ft) long and 6 cm (2$\frac{1}{2}$ in) thick; several arise from the base to form substantial clumps. Each stem has 6–7 prominent ribs with large, rounded, woolly areoles set about 3 cm (1$\frac{1}{4}$ in) apart and bearing 15 or more brownish-grey spines of varying lengths, some very short while others are 20 cm (8 in) or so in length. The yellow, funnel-shaped flowers, which are approximately 9 cm (3$\frac{1}{2}$ in) long and slightly more across when fully open, display numerous white stamens and a very short, thick style, as implied in the specific name.

### C. squarrosus

Previously known as *Erdisia squarrosa*, a species earlier described by F. Vaupel in 1913 as *Cereus squarrosus*, *C. squarrosus* is from mountainous country in eastern Peru. It is very sprawling in habit, with stems about 2 m (6 ft 6 in) in length, and a mere 2.5 cm (1 in) wide; they are more or less cylindrical in shape, with 8–9 shallow ribs and approximately 15 yellowish spines of unequal length emerging from the small areoles. The flowers, which are bright red in colour, appear towards the upper parts of the branches; they are 3–4 cm (1$\frac{1}{4}$–1$\frac{1}{2}$ in) in length and slightly wider when fully developed.

### C. brachypetalus

This would seem to be the tallest member of the genus, with stems and branches up to 4 m (13 ft) high. This, too, is a clump-forming species, branching from ground-level to form thick bushy plants. It was originally described in 1913 by Vaupel as *Cereus brachypetalus* and subsequently referred to *Corryocactus* by Britton and Rose in 1920. The ribs are very prominent, 7–8 in number, with large woolly areoles each producing about 20 black spines, varying in length from 1 cm ($\frac{3}{8}$ in) to 10 cm (4 in) or more long. The flowers are small, but attractive, only 6 cm ($2\frac{1}{2}$ in) wide when fully expanded, rich orange in colour, with short inner petals surrounding a broader throat.

Other more recent additions to the genus include *C. quadrangularis* from Peru, which was earlier included in *Erdisia*. This is another bushy species with stems more than 1 m (3 ft 3 in) long, each areole having 4–8 yellow radial spines, 2 cm ($\frac{3}{4}$ in) long and 3–4 centrals to 6 cm ($2\frac{1}{2}$ in). Flowers, about 5 cm (2 in) long, are a rich vermilion. *C. aureus* has shorter stems, about 50 cm (20 in) long, the spines are almost black, to 6 cm ($2\frac{1}{2}$ in) long; the 4 cm ($1\frac{1}{2}$ in) long flowers vary from yellow to rich red and appear laterally along the stems. This species, which is native to Arequipa in south Peru, was earlier called *Erdisia meyenii*.

# CORYPHANTHA

A genus closely linked to *Mammillaria*, but differing principally in having furrowed tubercles. The generic name was first used by Engelmann as a sub-genus of *Mammillaria,* and its generic status was established by Lemaire in 1868 when *Mammillaria sulcolanata* was named as the type species. At present, there are close on 80 species included in *Coryphantha*, and they occur from southern parts of Canada to southern parts of the United States and Mexico. The name is from the Greek *coryphe*, meaning top or crown, and *anthos*, meaning flower, re-referring to the flowers that appear from the top of the plants. The main characteristic, which is found in all species, is the furrow evident above each flower-bearing tubercle. Plants are either globular or cylindrical in shape, some solitary, others producing offsets to form clusters; they are tuberculate, with grooves or furrows. All are of easy culture, requiring a bright, sunny position and responding best at high temperatures in summer and never below 13°C (55°F) in winter. A normal cactus compost is suitable, with perhaps additional grit to make certain that the mixture is truly porous; water in moderation throughout spring and summer, and allow a totally dry dormancy period from November until April. Propagation can be achieved by removing offsets from clustering species and allowing them to callus for a few days before setting them in a very sandy loam mixture. Alternatively, all species can be grown from seeds.

## C. sulcolanata
From the Hidalgo region of Mexico. This more or less globular plant offsets fairly freely; each stem is about 5 cm (2 in) high and 6 cm ($2\frac{1}{2}$ in) thick. The tubercles are

*Coryphantha pseudoechinus*

angular at the base, but conical at the tip, with wool in the axils. Radial spines, up to 16 in number, brown with blackish tips and variable in size, are mainly spreading. Flowers are bright yellow, to about 8 cm (3 in) across, with similarly coloured stamens and whitish style and stigma lobes.

## C. pseudoechinus
A native of Coahuila, Mexico, and named by Böedecker, the plant is solitary or clustering, about 9 cm ($3\frac{1}{2}$ in) high and 5 cm (2 in) wide, grey-green in colour. Tubercles are about 1 cm ($\frac{3}{8}$ in) long, with woolly axils, 18–25 greyish-brown to almost black radial spines, about 1.5 cm ($\frac{5}{8}$ in) long, and a single longer central spine. The flowers, about 2 cm ($\frac{3}{4}$ in) long and 3 cm ($1\frac{1}{4}$ in) across, are violet-pink with paler margins to the petals and a greenish-yellow throat; stamens are whitish, and style and stigma lobes are yellow.

## C. erecta
One of the taller growing species, often 30 cm (1 ft) high and 8 cm (3 in) wide; the crown is particularly woolly, with yellowish spines. The tubercles do not exceed 1 cm ($\frac{3}{8}$ in) in length, axils and areoles are woolly, with 8–14 yellowish-brown, widely spreading radial spines more than 1 cm ($\frac{3}{8}$ in) long, and two to four longer centrals, one of which is decidedly curved. The glossy yellow flowers are 6 cm ($2\frac{1}{2}$ in) long and slightly wider; the stamens are yellow tipped with red; the style and stigma lobes are yellow.

## C. calipensis
From Puebla, Mexico, this is a generally clustering species, described by the Mexican botanist, Helia

Bravo-Hollis. The stems are greyish-green, to about 9 cm (3½ in) tall and 8 cm (3 in) diameter. The rather elongated tubercles are 3 cm (1¼ in) long and wide, with 10–16 yellow-brown radial spines and one central spine, all about 1.5 cm (⅝ in) in length. The flowers are glossy-yellow, often with a creamy sheen, approximately 6 cm (2½ in) wide; they have very attractive reddish stamens, and the style and stigma lobes are a bright yellow.

# CRYPTOCEREUS

This is an outstanding genus in as much as it contains a species with one of the most attractive of nocturnal flowers. It was first described in 1950 by E.J. Alexander and it could be the missing link between two subfamilies of the Cactaceae family, Hylocereanae and Epiphyllanae. Three species were originally contained within this genus, but two of these have been reclassified and placed in another genus. The plants are truly epiphytic, climbing by means of aerial roots, or just as content to hang pendent. The thick, flattish branches are deeply lobed, similar in many respects to *Epiphyllum darrahii* or *E. anguliger*. Provided a minimum temperature of 13°C (55°F) is maintained, they offer little or no problem in cultivation. If the plants are grown in a slightly shaded position and preferably elevated (as in a hanging-basket),

*Cryptocereus anthonyanus*

they will flourish and flower. A rich acid compost is advisable, with plenty of gritty sand added to ensure a porous mixture. Water should be given freely throughout the growing season; thereafter only a regular light spraying with tepid water is required. Propagation is by stem cuttings.

### C. anthonyanus
From Mexico, and named by Alexander for Dr Harold Anthony – apparently the first to flower species in cultivation – the branches are formed in loose clusters at intervals along the stem and are frequently 1 m (3 ft 3 in) or more long and up to 15 cm (6 in) across. They are deeply lobed, somewhat rounded at the tips, with areoles set at the base of the upper side of each lobe, each areole usually having three very short spines. The flowers, which appear in early summer, are about 12 cm (4½ in) long and 10–15 cm (4–6 in) across when fully open. They are sweetly scented. The inner petals are creamy-white, surrounded by cream-coloured petals with reddish-purple edges towards the base, and the outer segments are a bright reddish-brown-purple. The ovary is about 2 cm (¾ in) long; stamens, with cream-coloured filaments 1.5 cm (⅝ in) long; the style, of similar colour, is 7 cm (2¾ in) with 12–14 stigma lobes.

*Deamia testudo*

# DEAMIA

Another of the many genera raised by Britton and Rose in 1920 to contain only one species and previously named *Cereus testudo*. It is closely related to *Selenicereus*, and by some authorities it is considered almost inseparable. The plants are tree-climbing, stems and branches very variable in shape but all angled and jointed with areoles set closely along the margins of the ribs and bearing several fine, slender spines. In cultivation these epiphytic plants need a well-lit position but out of direct sun. Any proprietary cactus compost is suitable, provided that it is permeable. Provide supports for the climbing stems. Water thoroughly throughout the growing and flowering seasons, adding a liquid fertilizer every three weeks once the flower buds have formed. Maintain a minimum winter temperature of 13°C (55°F) and keep the plants almost dry. Propagation is by cuttings, in summer.

### D. testudo
So named from the humped appearance of many of the branch joints where they adhere by aerial roots to trees, which suggests the appearance of a tortoise shell and gives the species also its common name, tortoise cactus.

The length and diameter of the branch joints can vary considerably, and the wider ones have probably also given credence to the name. The flowers are nocturnal; they appear in spring, opening in the late afternoon or early evening, but they fade by morning. They are creamy-white in colour, about 28 cm (11 in) long with slender tubes, widening to about 20 cm (8 in) across. Stamens are numerous and the style about 25 cm (10 in) in length; they and the stigma-lobes are all creamy-white. The fruit that follows is reddish and densely covered with fine spines. In habitat this species has a scattered distribution in southern Mexico through to parts of Colombia.

### D. diabolica
Another purported species said to be native to Belize, the exact locality being Corozal. It differs but little from *D. testudo* except that the dull green branches have areoles set wider apart; the flowers are of a similar colour, as is the fruit.

# DISCOCACTUS

Plants of this genus were more or less unknown until the 1960s. The few plants whose names penetrated the sphere of cactus enthusiasts proved to be well-nigh unobtainable. When L. Pfeiffer established the genus in

1837 only three species were recorded; today about 15 are known, but they still remain very rare in collections and challenging to locate. The name is from the Greek *discos*, meaning a disc, which well describes the body shape, which is rather flattened on the top of what is otherwise a somewhat globular plant. In many ways they resemble *Melocactus*, especially in regard to the terminal cephalium, although they are not too closely related. All have rather pronounced ribs and attractive flowers, certainly larger than those of *Melocactus*. They are native to South America only – Brazil, Bolivia and Paraguay – and they come in many forms that are sometimes difficult to associate with each other.

These attractive but rare plants are among the most difficult cacti in cultivation. They are sun-loving plants, even though they are night-flowering. An ordinary cactus compost can be used, to which should be added further grit and some limestone chippings. Water carefully at all times, fairly regularly from May to September, then gradually moderate to complete dryness from November until April. A dilute fertilizer every three or four weeks in summer is beneficial. They will accept high temperatures in the growing season, and in winter anything less than 15°C (60°F) is likely to prove disastrous. Propagation is from seeds, but germination must take place in temperatures of 24–26°C (75–80°F)

### D. placentiformis

One of the original three species, when it was designated *D. insignis* by Pfeiffer. It was later discovered that the same species had been previously recorded as *Cactus placentiformis* and, that as the specific name had precedence, the present name can be said to date from 1894. The plant comes from the Rio de Janeiro region of Brazil. It is a low globular plant, with a rather flattened upper surface, bluish-green in colour, about 13 cm (5 in) in diameter. Ribs are low set and very broad, 10–14 in number with 5–8 areoles set along each; these bear 6–7 radial spines and occasionally a single central, the radials being more or less recurved and appressed to the stem. A rounded white woolly cephalium develops in maturity and from it appear large flowers with pinkish outer segments and white inner petals.

### D. horstii

From Minas Gerais, Brazil, this is one of the species introduced by Albert Buining and described by him and Brederoo. It is about the smallest within the genus, rarely exceeding 6 cm (2½ in) in diameter, even when grafted (which many enthusiasts tend to do). There are about 22 pronounced ribs surrounding the greyish-brown stem; the areoles are set fairly close together, each with 8–10 greyish-brown spines arranged in a comb-like formation. The cephalium, which is only

*Discocactus horstii*

about 2 cm (¾ in) across, consists of thick whitish wool and brown bristles. Flowers are up to 6 cm (2½ in) long, with yellow-brown outer segments and pure white inner petals.

### D. hartmannii

Another of the early-day species included in the genus by Britton and Rose, this was previously recorded as *Echinocactus hartmanni*. Native to Paraguay, it is a glossy-green plant about 15 cm (6 in) wide, somewhat flattened on the upper surface and so rarely exceeding 6 cm (2½ in) in height. It has 12–16 notched ribs, which form tubercle-like shapes along their length; the areoles have 8–12 yellow-grey radial spines and one central spine, 1–3 cm (⅜–1¼ in) long, mainly curved inwards. The cephalium is up to 4 cm (1½ in) high, somewhat tufted, and consisting of whitish wool and yellow or brownish, bristly spines. The flowers are about 5 cm (2 in) across when fully open, and 10 cm (4 in) long, with a slightly elongated tube; the outer segments are greenish-white, the inner petals white.

# DISOCACTUS

This genus was introduced by John Lindley in 1845 for just two species of epiphytic plants. In the same year G. Kunze proposed the name *Disisocactus* for the type species, *D. biformis*, both names indicating a particular feature apparent in this species – that both inner and outer flower segments are of equal length (the name comes from the Greek *dis*, meaning twice or double). Recent research by Myron Kimnach has resulted in other genera being merged with *Disocactus*, in particular *Chiapasia*, *Bonifazia*, *Lobeira* and a few species from *Rhipsalis* and *Pseudorhipsalis*. The genus *Wittia* (or *Wittiocactus*) is closely allied and might probably be reclassified within *Disocactus*. Many beautiful and unusual species are now mustered within this grouping; all are forest plants and enjoy a condition of filtered light in which to grow and flower successfully, preferably in hanging-baskets. A humid atmosphere is an advantage, together with a minimum temperature of 15°C (60°F) to ensure free flowering. An acid humus-rich compost is important, and it must be free-draining so as not to retain excess moisture. Water freely during the growing and flowering season, but sparingly at other times. Feed with a dilute fertilizer every three or four weeks during summer. Propagate by cuttings.

### D. biformis

Native to Honduras and Guatemala, this species has branches that are long and slender, often to 20 cm (8 in) or more, flat and leaf-like, with regular serrate margins. Areoles occur along the edges but are spineless, set within the teeth-like serrations. Flowers, borne during early spring, appear towards the tips of the branches; they are carried on slender tubes about 1 cm ($\frac{3}{8}$ in) long and consist of 8–9 segments each about 3 cm ($1\frac{1}{4}$ in) long, the outer petals spreading slightly and the inner petals remaining more or less erect. The flower colour is pale red; style and stamens are more red-purple and protrude beyond the petals; the 4–5 stigma lobes are creamy-white. The berry-like fruits which follow are rich wine-red.

### D. eichlamii

Initially described as *Phyllocactus* by Wilhelm Weingart in 1911, this was transferred by Britton and Rose to *Disocactus* in 1913. Native to Guatemala, it is a much branching species, each stem about 30 cm (1 ft) long and 5 cm (2 in) wide, thick and flat with margins strongly crenate. Flowers develop from areoles near the tips of the branches; they are slender, about 6 cm ($2\frac{1}{2}$ in) long, and a deep carmine-red. One of the most attractive species of the genus, its flowers open in succession over a period of many weeks, in late winter and spring. It makes a useful house plant.

### D. nelsonii

Previously known as *Chiapasia nelsonii*, this colourful flowering species, originating from Chiapas in Mexico and neighbouring Honduras, is quite rare in cultivation. Stems are long, flat and leaf-like, about 3 cm ($1\frac{1}{4}$ in) wide, and notched along the edges. The flowers are deep lilac-rose, beautifully scented and lasting for several days; they are trumpet-shaped and are borne on long smooth tubes, and they have an overall length of approximately 9 cm ($3\frac{1}{2}$ in).

*Disocactus nelsonii*

### D. macdougalli

Previously named *Lobeira macdougallii* by E.J. Alexander, who in so doing provided a new genus and a specific title denoting the discoverer of this very rare plant; it was later transferred to *Nopalxochia,* but is now placed where it rightfully belongs. A truly epiphytic species from southern Mexico, it has slender, thickish leaf-like stems, the margins regularly crenate. Flowers are lilac-pink, opening funnel-shaped and borne on long bracted tubes. Almost as rare is *D. quezaltecus*, native to the rain-forests of Guatemala, for which a new generic name, *Bonifazia*, was proposed and abandoned. It has flattened, pendent branches with pronounced reddish midribs and evenly marked crenate edges. The flowers are about 5 cm (2 in) long, trumpet-shaped, with reddish-purple petals and sepals, white-tipped red stamens and style.

# ECHINOCACTUS

This important genus was first described in 1827 by Heinrich Link and Otto, and it is considered that more than a thousand cacti have been ascribed to it. Later revisions have resulted in many species being transferred elsewhere, leaving comparatively few still identified with *Echinocactus*. At present it numbers nine species, all native to America, from the southerly areas of the United States to the central regions of Mexico. The name is from the Greek *echinos*, meaning hedgehog. They are all large, globular or widely cylindrical plants, mostly with many prominent ribs and fierce spines. Areoles are large and chiefly woolly, especially those in the crown. Compared with the enormous size of the plants, the flowers are relatively small, appearing around the upper

part of the body near the crown, or in the crown itself. Most species are easy to grow, given a position in full sun and a proprietary cactus compost with added loam or leaf-mould and sandy grit for quick drainage. Water during spring and summer, letting the plants dry between applications; feed every 3–4 weeks. From November until March withhold water and keep the plants at a minimum temperature of 10°C (50°F). Propagate by seed sown in late spring.

### E. grusonii

This species from Central Mexico, described by H. Hildmann in 1891, is called the golden barrel cactus because of its shape and its dense covering of golden spines. It has also been referred to as mother-in-law's cushion. The plant can reach well over 1 m (3 ft 3 in) in height and 80 cm (32 in) in diameter, but it takes many, many years to attain these proportions. Some 20–30 pronounced ribs reach from crown to base and are set regularly with areoles of yellowish wool, which gradually turns grey; they bear long and sharp golden spines,

*Echinocactus grusonii*

3–5 centrals and 8–10 radials. The flowers are somewhat cup-shaped, never opening wide, and they are not likely to appear until the plant has reached a very mature age. They are 5–6 cm ($2$–$2\frac{1}{2}$ in) long and about 5 cm (2 in) across, the outer petals are often brown externally, the inner petals are white or golden-yellow; they open only in full sunlight. This species develops its main features of golden spines and wool soon after seedling stage and these persist throughout its life. The varieties that are sometimes seen – *albispina*, with white spines, and *curvispina*, with slightly curved spines – are considered mutations and not, therefore, deserving of botanical status.

### E. ingens

Again from Central Mexico, and named by Zuccarini in 1837, *E. ingens* has had many names referred to it as synonyms, including *Echinocactus minax*. In maturity it can reach a height up to 1.5 m (5 ft) and a girth of some

*Echinocactus texensis*

1.25 m (4 ft). It is more or less globular in shape, generally greyish-green or greyish-purple in colour. As a young plant, the ribs are few in number, but as the plant develops they will muster 50 or more; they are straight, wide at the edges, along which are numerous yellowish, woolly areoles with protruding brown, rigid spines, about 8 radials and a single central, all 2–3 cm ($\frac{3}{4}$–$1\frac{1}{4}$ in) long. The flowers, produced at maturity, are yellow, about 3 cm ($1\frac{1}{4}$ in) long and 5 cm (2 in) across; the petals have a wax-like texture. Stamens and style are yellow, and the stigma lobes are reddish. This species needs a calcareous soil.

### E. polycephalus

Occurring in southern California, Nevada, Arizona and parts of northern Mexico, this was described by Engelmann and Jacob Bigelow in 1856. This species is rarely encountered in cultivation, particularly in Europe. It grows up to 80 cm (32 in) high and about 25 cm (10 in)

wide; commencing as an elongated, globular plant, it later begins to group freely and form very substantial clumps, which are greyish-green in colour, and are quite woolly in their individual crowns. There are 13–21 ribs, with areoles set along the edges and carrying yellowish-brown spines, which are mostly curved, 4–8 radials about 5 cm (2 in) long, and four rigid centrals to 9 cm ($3\frac{1}{2}$ in) in length. The yellow flowers are 5–6 cm ($2$–$2\frac{1}{2}$ in) long.

### E. texensis

First recorded by Carl Hopffer in 1842 under this name, it was later transferred by Britton and Rose to a new genus, *Homalocephala*, which is from the Greek and means flat or level-headed, referring to the rather flat appearance of the plant body. It has now been reinstated within *Echinocactus*. The plant, which is wider than it is tall in its natural habitat, is often 30 cm (1 ft) across and only 15 cm (6 in) high. The ribs, which are very pronounced, number 13–27, each rib having only 2–6 areoles. The spines are reddish, 5 cm (2 in) long, and there are 6–7 radials and a single central, which is often longer. Flowers appear in the crown of the plant; they are about 5 cm (2 in) long and wide, red and orange in the centre, the outer petals pinkish, always with lacerated edges. Stamens are red; style and stigma lobes are pale pink. The species has become extremely uncommon in recent years, having been systematically destroyed in its habitat in the interests of agriculture; it used commonly to be known as the horse crippler.

# ECHINOCEREUS

This is one of the most prominent genera within the Cactaceae and, as far as colourful flowers are concerned, one of supreme importance. The generic name, which is derived from the Greek *echinos,* meaning hedgehog, was established by G. Engelmann in 1848, and it was one of the very earliest genera of cacti to be established. All species are from Mexico and the United States; some remain more or less solitary throughout their lives, others form clusters of neat globular or semi-cylindrical stems, and yet others develop a trailing habit with stems becoming quite elongated. It is difficult to determine how many species comprise this popular genus as several have been relegated to synonymity with previously recorded species, while others have become varieties of already acceptable species.

They are among the easiest cacti in cultivation, requiring a truly sunny position, full exposure to sun being an advantage, especially in respect of flowering. Some species must have warmer conditions than others, but in general a minimum winter temperature of 7°C (45°F) will suit all of them. Careful watering must be observed; from April through to October water freely, although species that bloom earlier in the year should not be watered until the buds have formed and even then should not be watered overhead. Keep all plants completely dry during the winter months. Any proprietary cactus compost can be used or, for a homemade mixture, use equal parts of sterilized loam, decomposed leaf-mould, shredded peat and sharp gritty sand. All composts should be free-draining. Propagation is relatively easy from seeds sown early in the year in a prepared compost of equal parts sterilized loam, peat and sharp sand. They also can be multiplied by cuttings of offsets after the flowers have died.

### E. fendleri

The specific name was given by Engelmann as a *Cereus* in 1849, but it was reclassified by Rümpler in 1885. It occurs from Arizona and Texas to northern Mexico and is a tall-growing, clustering plant, sometimes to 20 cm (8 in)

*Echinocereus fendleri* var. *rectispinus*

*Echinocereus gentryii*

high with stems 5 cm (2 in) or more thick. The stems are fairly prominently ribbed, the areoles bearing 6–10 spreading radial spines and a single central, all differing in colour from pale yellow to almost black. Flowers, borne from the upper areoles, are a deep purple, each 8 cm (3 in) or more across and lasting for 3–4 days. A beautiful form of this species is found near the California/Nevada border; known as *E. fendleri* var. *rectispinus*, it has exquisite multi-coloured blooms in shades of pink, red and pale purple.

### E. gentryii

Found in the Sonora desert in northern Mexico, this species was named by E.U. Clover. It has a clustering group of thickish stems about 2.5 cm (1 in) wide. Ribs number about 5, the areoles set with a single central and up to 12 short brownish radial spines. Broadly bell-shaped flowers are about 8 cm (3 in) long and 5 cm (2 in) across, rich pink in colour.

### E. pentalophus

One of the better-known species, this is quite widespread in parts of Texas and northern Mexico. It has had many synonyms since it was first described as a *Cereus* by de Candolle in 1828. The stems are more or less procumbent, about 2 cm ($\frac{3}{4}$ in) thick with 5–6 pronounced ribs; the short spines, white with brownish tips, are few in number. Flowers are pink to reddish-purple, 12 cm ($4\frac{1}{2}$ in) long and wide, usually with a white throat, the petals delicately rounded at the tips.

### E. polyacanthus

Another clump-forming species, named by Engelmann, from parts of Chihuahua in Mexico and extending into southerly regions of the United States. The individual erect stems are about 20 cm (8 in) long and 6 cm ($2\frac{1}{2}$ in) thick, with about 10 low ribs. Areoles are closely set, with many reddish-brown or brownish-yellow spines, 2–5 cm ($\frac{3}{4}$–2 in) long, the spreading centrals longer than the radials. Flowers are funnel-shaped, about 6 cm ($2\frac{1}{2}$ in) long, in shades of pink and red.

### E. knippelianus

This, one of the few species that does not cluster, was described by C. Liebner; its specific name honours cactus authority Karl Knippel. From northern Mexico, it is rather oval in shape, about 10 cm (4 in) or more high and 5–6 cm (2–2$\frac{1}{2}$ in) thick; the 5–7 ribs are closely set, with tiny areoles, each sprouting a few yellowish, bristly spines 6 mm ($\frac{1}{4}$ in) long which fall very quickly. Flowers, about 4 cm (1$\frac{1}{2}$ in) long and wide, are pink with spreading petals, and have a distinctive cream-coloured style. The species is considered something of a rarity.

# ECHINOFOSSULOCACTUS

This remains one of the most difficult genera to comprehend sufficiently so as to make identification of individual species possible. It was established by George Lawrence in 1841, deriving its name from the Greek *echinos*, which refers to the spiny hedgehog appearance, and *fossula,* to emphasize the prominent furrows obvious between the ribs of most species. The name *Stenocactus* is much used in connection with these plants and was proposed by K. Schumann in 1898 when the species now classified under *Echinofossulocactus* were recorded as a sub-genus *Stenocactus* within *Echinocactus*. It is realistic to anticipate that this more pronounceable name will be botanically adopted. They are in the main heavily spined, globular plants, the rib formations varying considerably within the 10 or so species involved. All are native to Mexico. In cultivation they offer only few problems; they need really good light, an ordinary, fairly rich cactus compost and regular watering and feeding during the growing season. In winter they require a completely dry dormancy, at a minimum temperature of 70°C (45°F). They are easily grown from seeds sown early in the year.

### E. coptonogonus

The type species proposed by Lawrence is from the region of San Luis Potosí and probably from other central parts of Mexico. It is greyish-green in colour, about 10 cm (4 in) high and broad, with 10–15 broad, straight ribs that are deeply furrowed in between, with areoles bearing 3–5, horn-yellow spines about 3 cm (1¼ in) long and upward-pointing. Flowers appear from near or in the crown; they are about 3 cm (1¼ in) long and 4 cm (1½ in) across, white to lilac-purple with a pinkish-red line down the centre of the petals; the style is purplish with yellow-orange stamens.

### E. violaciflorus

Previously included in *Echinocactus* until reclassified by Britton and Rose, this is from Zacatecas in Mexico. It is invariably a globular plant, 8–10 cm (3–4 in) high and thick, grey to bluish-green in colour, with about 35 or more very wavy ribs mounted with greyish, woolly areoles set well apart. These bear 7, somewhat flattened and appressed spines, about 3 cm (1¼ in) long and 4 mm

*Echinocereus knippelianus*

(⅛ in) wide, inclined to curve slightly upwards or spread so as to form a dense spiny mass. Almost white or pale pink flowers are about 2.5 cm (1 in) long, with a pronounced violet median line, style and stamens.

The varying characteristics of the species provide an interesting subject, as scarcely any two are alike. *E. vaupelianus* is variable within itself, more so since *E. albatus* has been considered synonymous. It is a beautiful plant 9 cm (3½ in) thick, with 30–40 wavy ribs and white woolly areoles bearing up to 25 very thin, white radial spines about 1 cm (⅜ in) long and one or two dark brownish centrals, 7 cm (2¾ in) long. The yellowish-white or pinkish flowers are about 2 cm (¾ in) long.

# ECHINOPSIS

This is probably one of the most confusing genera of the Cactaceae. A number of other genera are so closely allied to *Echinopsis* as to be indistinguishable; certain genera have already been merged and others are likely to follow. However, the species described here are those that are truly recognized and accepted as being authentic plants within *Echinopsis*; others, such as *Lobivia, Setiechinopsis* and *Acanthocalycium* are described under their respective headings. The genus was established and described by Joseph G. Zuccarini in 1837 and at that time included only very few species. Here again the generic name comes from the Greek *echinos*, which, apart from meaning hedgehog, also means sea-urchin, and *opsis*, referring to appearance. This name would probably have described adequately the appearance of the plants known at that time, but now falls short of expressing the characteristics of the many species encompassed in *Echinopsis*. The species originally included were large, green, globular plants with few or many spines, bearing very large pinkish or white, invariably sweet-scented, trumpet-shaped flowers, which opened at night and were still visible the following day. More recently, species of *Trichocereus* and *Helianthocereus* have been given their place in *Echinopsis*; these are briefly mentioned under *E. huascha* below.

All species are relatively easy in cultivation. They will succeed in producing good growth and many flowers if

*Echinopsis aurea*

given a really bright position, a minimum temperature in winter not below 10°C (50°F) and a correct soil balance. Water freely throughout spring and summer, but never to the extent that the soil becomes too wet and remains so; during the dormancy period from November until March give no water at all. Any good proprietary cactus compost is suitable; it is essential that the mixture is thoroughly porous. Regular feeding at monthly intervals during the growing season helps to achieve healthy plants and encourage excellent flowering. Propagate by offsets in summer or by seeds sown in late winter or early spring.

Reference must be made to the adaptability of many *Echinopsis* to cross-pollinate with species of other genera, such as *Lobivia*. The results have made possible numerous glamorous, extremely colourful hybrids, which are lovely to look at and easy to grow. They are often offered by specialist nurseries as 'Sussex Hybrids' or 'Paramount Hybrids', and they include beautiful colour forms.

### E. eyriesii

From Argentina, Brazil and Uruguay, this, one of the best-known, species was included in the genus by Zuccarini in 1839 and is perhaps typical of an *Echinopsis*-looking plant. Similar in appearance to a sea-urchin, the plant is generally globular, becoming slightly

columnar with age, to about 15 cm (6 in) tall and 12 cm (4½ in) thick. There are 12–18 ribs, with woolly rounded areoles bearing up to 10 radial spines and 8 centrals. The flowers are the prime feature, pure white in colour, opening in late afternoon and filling the night air with perfume; they are large and trumpet-shaped, 17–25 cm (6¾–10 in) long. Other very similar species, sometimes confused with *E. eyriesii*, include *E. multiplex*, with pinkish flowers, and *E. oxygona*, whose flowers are more reddish. The lovely *E. imperialis*, wih its splendid white blooms, is probably of hybrid origin.

### E. aurea
Discovered by J. N. Rose in Córdoba, Argentina, in 1915, this has distinctive bright yellow funnel-shaped flowers, the inner petals an even deeper shade; they are about 9 cm (3½ in) long and, unusually for this genus, day-flowering. Plants are about 10 cm (4 in) high with a diameter of about 7 cm (2¾ in); they remain solitary. The ribs, about 14 in number, are prominent and set with brownish areoles carrrying 8–10 pale brown radial spines and one or several centrals of blackish-brown. This species has been cross-pollinated with species of *Epiphyllum* to develop yellow-flowering *Epiphyllum* hybrids.

### E. huascha
Native to Catamarca in Argentina, this has been included in several genera before being retained in *Echinopsis*. While it was initially described as *Cereus huascha* it has been better known as *Helianthocereus* or *Trichocereus*. It is a plant with stems to nearly 1 m (3 ft 3 in) high, cylindrical in shape and about 5 cm (2 in) wide; it quickly forms quite extensive clumps, especially in its natural habitat. The stems often have as many as 18 ribs, each areole having one or two brownish central spines, about 6 cm (2½ in) long, and several very small radials. The funnel-shaped flowers, about 10 cm (4 in) long, are richly coloured in red or deep yellow.

# ENCEPHALOCARPUS

This fascinating monotypic genus was established by Alwin Berger in 1929. The name comes from three Greek words: *en* meaning in, *kephale*, which signifies head, and *karpos*, meaning fruit and probably referring to the fruits that, like the flowers, are produced in the crown or head of the plant. It is closely related to *Ariocarpus* and *Pelecyphora*, and taxonomists suggest that it might well prove to be synonymous with the latter. The whole body forms a truly globular plant, covered completely with thick scale-like tubercles, broadly three-sided; the keel on the undersurface of each tubercle is an important and distinctive characteristic. The tubercles

are closely appressed so as to totally obscure the actual plant body. Cultivation requirements are similar to those for *Ariocarpus*.

### E. strobiliformis
Previously recorded by Werdemann as an *Ariocarpus* species, which is understandable as there are many similarities in the general appearance, this is found in quite a restricted area of Tamaulipas in Mexico, growing on hot sunny hillsides. The specific name means the cone or *strobilus* associated with conifers, and this aptly describes the shape. The plant is 6 cm (2½ in) across, greyish-green in colour. Areoles occur on the inner side of the tubercles; they are oval and very woolly, with minute spines. Flowers, produced from the areoles of the youngest tubercles in the crown of the plants, are bright violet-red in colour and about 4 cm (1½ in) across, the petals slightly toothed at the tips; stamens and style are yellow with 3–5 stigma lobes.

# EPIPHYLLUM

A genus of epiphytic cacti established by Adrian Hardy Haworth in 1812. The name is derived from the Greek *epi*, meaning on, and *phyllon*, a leaf, because early botanists considered that the flower came from the leaf. The stem is, of course, very leaf-like, a fact that obviously caused confusion at the time. The name *Phyllocactus* was at one time used for this group of cacti; this, too, is from the Greek and means leaf cactus. Here, also, the appearance of the stem is the decisive factor even though it is never a leaf. Yet another name emerged in 1898: *Euphyllocactus*, the *eu* meaning good or complete. Misunderstandings have abounded over the years.

There would appear to be 17 recognized species in the genus, although this figure may vary according to the authority. The main centre of distribution is in Mexico and Central America, invariably in close proximity to forested areas and more often than not in the rain-forests themselves. They have a main woody stem which carries somewhat flattened branches, some fairly smooth-edged, others with deep notches or crenations. Along these edges the areoles occur and from these the flowers appear. Some species flower nocturnally, others diurnally; the flowers are all large, principally white or cream, and frequently beautifully scented.

In the 1950s an important discovery was made in the region of Chiapas in southern Mexico, in dense rain-forest. It had a stem 30 cm (1 ft) wide, completely flat with a strong midrib along its length, and the edges lobed deeply, to about 15 cm (6 in). The American botanist E.J. Alexander described this as *Epiphyllum chrysocardium* because of its extraordinary flower, which is often called Heart of Gold, so large and impressive is it – about

*Encephalocarpus strobiliformis*

20 cm (8 in) wide and 30 cm (1 ft) long. A new generic name, *Marniera*, was later introduced for this species and for *E. macropterum* in honour of L. Marnier-Lapostelle, one of the most outstanding plantsmen involved with succulent plants. It has now, however, sunk into synonymity with *Epiphyllum*.

Epiphyllums need a position with good, but filtered light, out of direct sun, especially in summer. Being forest plants, they also enjoy a humid atmosphere; indoors this can be achieved with overhead mist sprays of tepid water. The best growing medium is an acid cactus compost with additional leaf-mould; ensure that it is free-draining. Water freely from spring to autumn, less so in winter when the plants should be kept at 10°C (50°F), but never let them dry out completely. Feed every two weeks during the growing season. The magnificent flowers, which have given epiphyllums their common name of orchid cactus, are diurnal in most species and hybrids, and nocturnal in others; they are borne in spring and early summer. Propagation is by cuttings.

### E. ackermannii

Thought by some authorities to belong to *Nopalxochia*, as it has been found growing in the wild south of Oaxaca and elsewhere in the area of Chiapas. It may be a true species, or perhaps a hybrid of *Nopalxochia phyllanthoides* and *Heliocereus speciosus*, another Mexican cactus but not epiphytic. It has wavy, slightly notched, flattened and elongated stems and bears bright scarlet flowers about 12 cm (4¾ in) long; they open during the day in spring and early summer. The species differs from the 'cottage-window' plant of the same name, which has been popular as a house plant for many years; this is indeed a hybrid with angular stems, but apparently not truly reproduced by present-day hybridizers.

### E. cartagense

Described by Britton and Rose in 1913, this is a much taller, elongated species, growing to 3 m (10 ft) in length. It is found in the rain-forests of Costa Rica, and other adjoining countries. The stems are thin and flat with regular deep crenations along the edges with the areoles being quite pronounced. The flowers open at night, with pure white inner petals and orange-pink or yellowish outer petals; they measure 10 cm (4 in) or slightly more across, and are borne on slender pinkish-red tubes about 15 cm (6 in) long. This is one of the more uncommon species and can prove quite variable in flower size and colour.

### E. crenatum

Recorded within this genus by G. Don in 1855, this is from Guatemala and Honduras, and when originally described in 1844 was called *Cereus crenatus*. It is one of the better-known species, of erect habit and densely branched. The stems are thick and sturdy, though inclined to thin towards the edges, which have fairly deep crenations. The flowers are creamy-yellow, often with a pale greenish tint showing, about 20 cm (8 in) across and carried on greenish-red tubes; the stamens are pale yellow and the style is white. The species can be variable in growth or flower. The form 'Chichicastenango' has deep and long crenations on the branches; another, 'Kinchinjunga', differs very much, especially when in bud, from

the type plant. Both of these are recorded from differing forest areas of Guatemala.

All species are worthy of mention, but particularly outstanding is *E. darrahii*, previously included in *Phyllocactus*. This is from southern Mexico and has attractively notched branches to form pronounced lobes. The flowers are about 18 cm (7 in) long and 8 cm (3 in) across, pure white in all parts except for the outer petals, which are tinted yellow.

Several species have numerous, very slender petals; they are principally distinguishable from each other by the colour of the style: in *E. stenopetalum* it is carmine-red, while *E. strictum* has a partly pink, partly white style. *E. pittieri* has white flowers with a strong scent of hyacinths; the style is pinkish. All three are from Central America and were incorporated in the genus in 1913. *E. laui* is one of the more recently named species and native to southern Mexico. It is a low-growing, sturdy plant with very large white flowers and contrasting pinkish sepals.

*Epiphyllum strictum*

Numerous, beautifully coloured hybrids and cultivars have resulted from crossing species of *Epiphyllum* with those of other genera. The list of names runs into thousands, and many have been officially recorded through the medium of the Epiphyllum Society of America; on the other hand, numerous cultivars have not received the same attention and could possibly be duplications of 'official' hybrids. Hybridizing of these exotics appears to have started about 1834 in Britain, when a hybrid named 'Jenkinsonii' made its appearance. This has deep scarlet flowers, possibly due to the inclusion of a *Heliocereus* in its parentage. Cultivars with flowers of many colours and shades, including multi-coloured, are available: white, cream, yellow, orange, pink, red, purple, violet in differing shades. With scarcely an exception they have all proved floriferous and fine house plants, including the following: 'Barbara Driver', large lilac-pink flowers with carmine throats; 'Discovery', semi-pendent stems with light yellow long-lasting flowers; 'Dobson Yellow', very

*Epiphyllum* 'Barbara Driver'

large flowers with spreading petals in shades of yellow; 'Gloria', compact flowers in shades of fuchsia, short tubes; 'Professor Ebert', deep lilac-pink; and 'Royal Token', with very large, brilliant orange-red flowers.

# EPITHELANTHA

This monotypic genus was named by Dr F.A.C. Weber in 1898 but not formally published until Britton and Rose confirmed it in 1922. The generic name, from the Greek *epi*, meaning on, *thele* for nipple and *anthos* for flower, indicates that the flower is borne on a tubercle. The small globular plants are covered with numerous tubercles in rather spiralling rows, bearing densely set spines. The tubercles suggest a close relationship with *Mammillaria*, and the species was indeed at one time included in that genus; the principal difference is that in *Epithelantha* the flowers arise from the spine areoles, not from the axils. In cultivation they require a warm sunny position throughout the year. A porous, rich calcareous soil is necessary; water moderately throughout the warmest months, but keep the plants completely dry during the dormant season from November until late March. A minimum temperature of 10°C (50°F) is advisable in winter. Propagation is by seed sown in late winter.

### E. micromeris

This was described as a *Mammillaria* in 1856. It is a variable species from areas of Texas to parts of Coahuila and Nuevo León in Mexico and uncommon in cultivation. Plants may remain solitary or form clusters; each stem measures about 6 cm ($2\frac{1}{2}$ in) in diameter and is covered with tubercles each with about 20 tiny white spines which radiate and give the whole plant a silvery sheen. Flowers are borne at the tips of the plants, from young tubercles with minute areoles; they are small, white or pinkish, with only few petals and stamens. Fruits are in the form of club-shaped berries, red in colour and remaining on the plant up to one year before maturing; they contain small black seeds.

# ERIOCEREUS

This was the original generic name used by A. Berger until the few species were reclassified as *Harrisia*. It seems likely that they will revert to *Harrisia* if current taxonomy exerts itself, as there is little, if any, real difference in characteristics between *Eriocereus* and *Harrisia*. The name is from the Greek *erion,* meaning wool, and would seem to refer to the woolly tube of the flowers.

Above: *Epiphyllum* 'Discovery'

Opposite above: *Epithelantha micromeris*; opposite below: *Eriocereus bonplandii*

Below left: *Epiphyllum* 'Dobson Yellow'; below right: *Epiphyllum* 'Royal Token'

They are slender columnar plants, all native to South America, with something of a climbing habit, and branching quite freely. The nocturnal flowers are large, borne from the terminal part of the branches. They are of easy culture and are more or less undemanding as far as close attention is concerned. A good bright position is advisable, but not necessarily in full sun. An open, fairly acid compost should be used. Water freely in the growing period, but maintain a dry winter dormancy, at a minimum temperature of 10°C (50°F). Propagation is by cuttings or seeds. Certain species have been used successfully as grafting stock for weaker species such as *Frailea*.

### E. bonplandii
Referred to as *Cereus bonplandii* in 1837, reclassified within *Harrisia* and then (by Riccobono) in *Eriocereus*, this native of Brazil, Paraguay and Argentina has bluish-green stems, about 3 m (10 ft) long and 8 cm (3 in) thick, semi-erect, clambering or trailing in habit. The 4 or more low ribs provide rather angled stems, the edges with areoles set about 2 cm ($\frac{3}{4}$ in) apart and bearing 6–10 reddish-grey spines about 4 cm ($1\frac{1}{2}$ in) in length. The trumpet-shaped flowers, 25 cm (10 in) long and 20 cm (8 in) across at the tips, are reddish-green externally, with inner white petals and numerous white stamens. The fruits which follow are edible, about 6 cm ($2\frac{1}{2}$ in) in diameter, spineless and containing numerous black seeds.

### E. martinii
This Argentine species is probably the best known species. It was first described, by J. Labouret, as *Cereus*, then it became *Eriocereus*, followed by *Harrisia*, and it is currently back in *Eriocereus*. It is a branching, clambering species with slender stems 2 m (6 ft 6 in) or more long and not exceeding 5 cm (2 in) in width. There are 4–5 wide ribs with about 6 very short radial spines and one central, up to 3 cm ($1\frac{1}{4}$ in ) long. Flowers are about 20 cm (8 in) long, 10 cm (4 in) or more wide at the tips, pale greenish externally, white inner petals, and a green style.

# ERIOSYCE

When this genus was established by R.A. Philippi in 1872, it was for one species alone; today there are possibly 6–7 accepted species. The name is derived from the Greek *erion*, meaning wool, and *sykon*, meaning fig, referring to the woolly fruits. The genus of *Rodentiophila* is synonymous, and it is closely allied to *Neoporteria*. All species are native to South America. The plants are quite large and globular with numerous ribs and bell-shaped flowers with fine bristly and spiny tubes; the fruits are oblong in shape, very spiny, and shed their seeds through a basal pore. Plants are of quite easy culture, requiring a bright, sunny location with minimum humidity, free watering throughout the period from April to October, then dry for the winter months, at a minimum temperature of 10°C (50°F). Feeding is recommended at three to four weekly intervals in the growing season. Propagation is from seeds sown between January and March in any proprietary seed compost.

### E. ceratistes
The type species was earlier recorded as *Echinocactus ceratistes* by Otto in 1837 and as *Eriosyce sandillon* by Philippi in 1872. It is found in mountainous areas in Chile and Argentina at about 2000 m (6500 ft). Plants in their natural habitats can attain a height of 1 m (3 ft 3 in) and a girth of up to 50 cm (20 in). The 20–35 ribs are woolly, more so towards the crown and set with large areoles bearing up to 20 yellowish-brown spines, 3.5 cm ($1\frac{3}{8}$ in) long, mainly straight but sometimes curved. The bell-shaped flowers are freely borne, about 3.5 cm ($1\frac{3}{8}$ in) long, carmine-red at first, then fading to pale yellowish-red. This is a variable species and several varietal names are ascribed to it.

### E. rodentiophila
Previously included in Ritter's *Rodentiophila*, this can reach 60 cm (2 ft) or more in height and about 30 cm (1 ft) in diameter. The number of ribs varies from 19 to 35, having areoles with many pale reddish-brown spines, 12–15 radials and 5–12 centrals. Flowers, up to 4 cm ($1\frac{1}{2}$ in) long, are purple with creamy-white margins. It is native to Antofagasta, Chile.

# ERYTHRORHIPSALIS

This comprises just one unique plant which is native to the São Paulo and Rio de Janeiro regions of Brazil, where it inhabits forests and grows epiphytically. The genus was introduced by A. Berger in 1920, when the species was transferred from *Rhipsalis* where it had previously been placed. The generic name is from the Greek *erythros*, which refers to the fruits, which are ultimately red; the fruits of *Rhipsalis* are generally considered whitish. It is an excellent plant for hanging-basket culture. It needs a predominantly acid compost, a position in filtered light out of direct sun and to be kept moderately moist throughout the year. Winter temperature should be not less than 13°C (55°F) because it very often produces its flowers in early to mid-winter. Propagation is by cuttings.

### E. pilocarpa
Of semi-pendent habit, this species has cylindrical

*Erythrorhipsalis pilocarpa*

occur from the tips of the branches; they have very short scaly tubes with yellowish-white petals and whitish stamens and style. Fruits, with many small bristles, are greenish but becoming wine-red and containing seeds larger than those of *Rhipsalis*. Whether this characteristic justifies separation from *Rhipsalis* is doubtful, and it does not seem inappropriate to place it back in that genus.

# ESCOBARIA

The name commemorates Romulo and Numa Escobar, distinguished Mexican brothers of the 19th and 20th centuries. It was established by Britton and Rose in 1923 and today comprises about 12 species which are native to the southern United States and northern Mexico. Individual plants are globular or partially cylindrical, but are generally found in clusters on hill sides and low mountain slopes. The genus is closely related to *Mammillaria* and *Coryphantha*. Plants are reasonably easy in cultivation, but are best given a really sunny and airy position, free of draughts, or they may be liable to lose their attractive features. Any proprietary cactus compost can be used, provided that it is porous with ample gritty sand added. Water in moderation throughout the summer months – as the plants dislike wet feet, any surplus water should be poured away or rot may set

stems and branches in whorls about 12 cm (4½ in) long. They are greyish-green in colour, with 8–10 very shallow, indistinct ribs, closely set areoles, each areole with 3–10 tiny greyish, bristly spines. The flowers, about 2.5 cm (1 in) across when fully open, usually

*Escobaria chaffeyi*

in. Keep totally dry from November until late March and maintain a minimum temperature of 10°C (50°F). Propagation by seeds in late winter or offsets in summer.

### E. tuberculosa

Initially placed in *Mammillaria* by Engelmann, this became the type species when the genus was created in 1923. It is widespread in many parts of the southern United States and north Mexico. A clump-forming plant, which can be most variable, particularly in the spination. Stems are cylindrical, 10–18 cm (4–7 in) high and up to 6 cm (2½ in) wide, covered with spirally arranged tubercles, woolly axils and areoles, the latter bearing 20–30 brownish-white radial spines, about 1 cm (⅜ in) long, and 5–9 centrals which are longer and black-tipped. Flowers are borne in the axils; they are about 2.5 cm (1 in) across, with pale pink inner petals and deeper outer segments; the stamens are reddish or white, the style and stigma lobes yellow.

### E. chaffeyi

Discovered in Zacatecas, Mexico, by Dr Elswood Chaffey and named for him by Britton and Rose, the species has stems about 12 cm (4½ in) high and 5–6 cm (2–2½ in) wide, with many low-set tubercles bearing a dense covering of numerous bristly white, spreading radial spines and a number of centrals, which are tipped brownish-black. The flowers, about 1.5 cm (⅝ in) long and a little less across, are creamy-yellow with a brownish central line down each petal; stamens and style are white and the stigma lobes greenish-yellow. Other species include the miniature *E. roseana*, native to Coahuila, Mexico, which is only about 4 cm (1½ in) high and 3 cm (1¼ in) across, with yellowish radial and central spines and reddish-white flowers. It was originally placed in *Thelocactus* by Böedecker and later transferred, by Backeberg, to *Escobaria*.

# ESPOSTOA

A genus of beautifully spined, columnar cacti established by Britton and Rose in 1920, which today would appear to include *Thrixanthocereus* and *Vatricania*. Species earlier included in *Pseudoespostoa* have already been reclassified into this genus. It is named after Nicolas E. Esposto, a 20th century botanist from Lima in Peru. The species resemble *Cephalocereus* and *Oreocereus* as far as elegant stem growth is concerned, but otherwise they vary in several respects. Plants are native to Ecuador, Bolivia and northern Peru, at altitudes to more than 2000 m (6500 ft). Many develop tree-like proportions, others are more bushy. Spination is always of interest and attraction, perhaps even more so as a cephalium or pseudocephalium develops with maturity. Nocturnal

*Espostoa lanata*

flowers appear from the cephalium, and in some the smell is rather unpleasant. Cultivation presents few or no problems, and if essential requirements are met, the plants can be grown to perfection. A light sunny position must be provided, and a good enriched cactus compost is important as ample nourishment is necessary in order to produce really attractive specimens. Watering, throughout the growing and flowering season, with a dilute liquid feed every 3–4 weeks must be undertaken with care, allowing a short drying-out period between waterings. Keep dry in winter, at a minimum temperature of 10°C (50°F). Propagation is from seeds.

### E. lanata

First described by Humboldt, Bonpland and Knuth in 1823 as *Cactus lanatus*, this is the type species. It has also been known as *Oreocereus*, *Cleistocactus* and *Pilocereus*. On the arid hills of Ecuador and north Peru, it can reach tree-like growth to about 4 m (13 ft) tall and 15 cm (6 in) thick. In cultivation, it generally remains a single columnar plant, eventually about 2 m (6 ft 6 in) high, with 20 or more ribs set closely together and areoles bearing about 12 clear whitish-yellow or reddish short radial spines and one or two red-tipped white centrals, 8 cm (3 in) long, densely covered with white or creamy-white hairs that envelop the whole stem structure. Mature plants have white flowers, to 6 cm (2½ in) long, appearing laterally from the attractive pseudocephalium.

### E. senilis

Described by Ritter as a *Thrixanthocereus* species, it was subsequently transferred to the present genus. This native of north Peru has, in the natural habitat, long, slender stems, 2–4 m (6 ft 6 in–13 ft) in length, and about 6 cm (2½ in) diameter, forming bushy clumps. There are about 18 ribs with numerous radial and central spines all about 1 cm (⅜ in) long; a few of the centrals are more prominent, to 4 cm (1½ in) long and reddish-brown in colour, the remainder are white, densely surrounded with numerous white woolly hairs that completely cover the stems. The flowers are a rich purple-red, about 6 cm (2½ in) long, and protruding from the thick brownish cephalium which, in maturity, forms terminally on the stem.

### E. haagei

At one time included by Backeberg in *Pseudoespostoa*, this is also from Peru. It is a branching species, principally from the base, with greyish-green stems and up to 30 low ribs. The areoles bear numerous spines intermixed with dense white hairs that cover the whole stems. This 'coating' is especially pronounced at the tips. The flowers are white. It may be synonymous with *E. melanostele*.

# EULYCHNIA

This is one of the earliest genera of the Cactaceae, established in 1860 by Rudolph Philippi for a few very striking South American plants, native to Chile and Peru, where they are mainly found on dry arid hillsides. The name is from the Greek *eu*, meaning well, and *lychnos*, meaning torch or candle. It is difficult to comprehend how this applies to the species, unless perhaps to the candle-like, slender erect growth of younger plants, or to the fact that the branches of older specimens are used as firewood by the local population. The genus *Philippicereus* is considered synonymous. In general, they are tall columnar plants, some almost tree-like, others forming bushy clumps. Flowers appear from near the terminal ends of the stems and are unusual in that the floral tubes are very short or lacking entirely; they also have a peculiar characteristic of a dense covering of bristles or scales on the outer surface, sometimes woolly. These very attractive species are quite easy to cultivate successfully, requiring a position in good light, an ordinary cactus compost and moderate watering throughout the growing and flowering season. Feeding is advisable only at

*Eulychnia acida*

4-weekly intervals between May and September. Keep the plants completely dry during dormancy, at a minimum winter temperature of 10°C (50°F). Propagation is from seeds.

### E. breviflora

Found in Coquimbo, Chile, this was named by Philippi as the type species. It is perhaps better known as *E. spinibarbis*. A many-branched plant, sometimes 4 m (13 ft) tall in its wild habitat, with branches 6–7 cm (2½–2¾ in) thick. There are 10–13 ribs with areoles bearing about 20 or more dark brownish-grey radial spines, about 3 cm (1¼ in) long and 3–6 similarly coloured centrals, 15 cm (6 in) in length. The flowers, 8 cm (3 in) long, are white or pale pinkish.

### E. acida

A tall-growing plant, 5 m (16 ft 6 in) or more high, with few or several more or less terminal branches. It is from western Chile (Choapa to Copiapó) and was named by Philippi in 1864 and described by Schumann as *Cereus acidus* in 1903. Each stem has about 12 rounded ribs set with brown areoles, about 3 cm (1¼ in) apart, carrying many greyish radial spines, about 5 cm (2 in) in length, and 1–4 very long centrals, up to 20 cm (8 in) long. Short scaly floral tubes, about 5 cm (2 in) long, open to pinkish flowers about 13 cm (5 in) across at the tip.

# FACHEIROA

A genus established by Britton and Rose in 1920 and containing a single species. The generic name is taken from a Brazilian word for cacti, *facheiro*. In a current revision, species previously included in *Zehntnerella* have been brought into *Facheiroa*, thus forming a group of about five species, all of which are native to Brazil. The name of Leo Zehntner, a Brazilian botanist, must be mentioned here. His name was recorded and honoured in the genus *Zehntnerella*, and he was also the discoverer of the first species of *Facheiroa*, which has a close affinity with *Leocereus*. Plants are columnar, tree-like or sometimes semi-prostrate and forming bushy clumps; the stems are often several metres in length. The nocturnal flowers are generally quite small and appear from the pseudo-cephalium which mainly develops towards the tips of the stems. These are uncommon plants, very suited to the connoisseur, but because of their size ample room is necessary to enable the plants to develop. An ordinary cactus compost provides a suitable growing medium, but it must be very porous. They prefer a really bright position, not necessarily in full sun, but certainly not in shade. Water freely from May to September, allowing a short drying-out period between waterings; give a liquid fertilizer every 4 weeks during this period. Keep barely moist in winter, at a temperature not below 13°C (55°F). Propagation is by cuttings or seeds.

### F. publiflora

The better name for this species may be that given to it by Werdemann – *Facheiroa ulei*. It comes from Bahia and has stems up to 5 m (16 ft 6 in) and about 12 cm (4¾ in) thick, with more slender branches, to only 7 cm (2¾ in) in diameter. There are about 15, low-set ribs with brown-felted areoles, about 1 cm (⅜ in) apart, along the edges from which the brownish spines appear, 10–15 radials, 1.5 cm (⅝ in) long, and three or four centrals, 2.5 cm (1 in) in length. Pseudocephalium, about 20 cm (8 in) long and 4 cm (1½ in) broad, forms at the top of the stems and consists of a dense mass of short brownish bristles; the flowers appear from here. They are white or pinkish-white, and approximately 4.5 cm (1¾ in) long and 2 cm (¾ in) wide.

### F. squamulosa

From Bahia, and earlier recorded, by Gürke, as *Cereus squamulosus* and, by Britton and Rose, as *Zehntnerella squamulosa*, this is a tall, slender plant that branches freely from near the base on a quite short trunk about

20 cm (8 in) thick. The branches are only 7 cm (2¾ in) thick, but spreading, often to a length of 4 m (13 ft) or more; they each have 17–20 ribs closely set with rounded areoles bearing 10–15 brownish spines each about 3 cm (1¼ in) long; white flowers, about 3 cm (1¼ in) long, appear from the terminal sides of the stems.

# FEROCACTUS

These are mainly large globular plants, and with age many can reach well over 1 m (3 ft 3 in) high, becoming almost cylindrical in shape. The name was established by Britton and Rose in 1922, from the Latin *ferox* or *ferus*, meaning wild or fierce, and referring to the spiny character of all the species. The genus is closely allied to *Echinocactus*, which at one time included a number of the species, but differs in having very short flower tubes, the flowers being produced almost from the crown of the plant. The spination is another characteristic, perhaps more evident in some species than in others, with a very thick, wide and hooked central spine, which is often highly colourful. All species are native to southern regions of the United States, Mexico and Guatemala. The plants are very slow-growing, but with care can be grown to quite spectacular dimensions, though they are never likely to attain their ultimate proportions in the lifetime of a mere human; it is certain that many of those that have developed a columnar form are well over 200 years old. A truly sunny position is essential as this enhances the chances of colourful spines. Use a cactus compost plus additional loam as a growing medium, and make sure that the mixture is thoroughly porous. Water regularly during the summer months, adding liquid fertilizer every three weeks. During dormancy let the soil become completely dry and maintain a constant temperature of 10°C (50°F). Propagation is by seeds.

### F. wislizenii

The type species when the genus was established. It occurs from parts of Arizona and Texas through to Sonora and Chihuahua in northern Mexico and Baja California. It is globular at first, but with age becomes cylindrical to about 2 m (6 ft 6 in) high and a girth of 80 cm (32 in). It has 15–25 ribs, about 3 cm (1¼ in) high, with large areoles that are brownish-yellow and woolly at first, and from which emerge 15–20 bristly yellowish radial spines and about 4 flat, ringed and thick centrals, 5 cm (2 in) long; one of these is always fiercely hooked at the tip, at first brownish-yellow but gradually darkening. The flowers are 5–6 cm (2–2½ in) long, yellow or orange with a greenish tube, while stamens, style and stigma lobes are bright yellow. The yellow fruits are oblong, 5 cm (2 in) long and scaly, containing many black, slightly pitted seeds.

### F. townsendianus

The specific title acknowledges the work of Charles H. Townsend, a Director of the New York Aquarium, who had much to do with the discovery of the plant. It comes from Baja California and the off-shore islands. It rarely exceeds 40 cm (16 in) in height or girth, and it is dark to greyish-green in colour, with about 16 obtuse ribs which are often slightly spiralled and notched. Large and woolly areoles are set between the notches, bearing 8–9 slender radial spines, 3 cm (1½ in) long, and about five greyish-brown centrals which are partially hooked at the tips. The flowers are 5–6 cm (2–2½ in) long; the outer petals are red with yellow edges, the inner pinker with green-yellow margins. Stamens and style are deep pink, stigma lobes pale green.

### F. fordii

Another of the smaller-growing species, this may attain 40 cm (16 in) in height, but only up to 15 cm (6 in) in diameter, often much less. This, too, is from Baja California and occasionally found in Sonora. A greyish-green plant with about 20 ribs, woolly areoles which bear about 15 spreading, needle-like radial spines and 4 centrals, the longest outward pointing, flat, about 4 cm (1½ in) long and very hooked; this is pale red and contrasts well with the other whitish spines. Flowers, which are about 4 cm (1½ in) long, have pink inner petals, pale pink stamens, and white or yellowish style and stigma lobes.

### F. acanthodes

Another popular and well-known species is *F. acanthodes*, which is variable in spine colouring according to habitat; it is widespread from the California/Nevada border to parts of Baja California and Sonora. This is a globular plant when young, but can reach to 3 m (10 ft) in maturity. Heavily spined, varying in colour from whitish to reddish-brown, the centrals are longer than the radials and curved. The flowers are yellow or orange; stamens, style and stigma lobes are yellowish.

*Ferocactus townsendianus*

*F. latispinus*

From the eastern and central regions of Mexico, this is another favourite. It is a high-altitude plant, found above 3000 m (10,000 ft). The reddish radial and central spines are characteristic, especially the long, ringed lower central which is hooked, 4 cm (1½ in) or more long and 6 mm (¼ in) wide. Flowers are white or reddish-lilac in colour.

# FRAILEA

A most fascinating genus of somewhat dwarf plants, closely related to both *Parodia* and *Notocactus*, it was established in 1922 by Britton and Rose, and named for a Spanish-American, Manvel Fraile, of the US Department of Agriculture, Washington. The species number 30 or more and all are native to South America. They are small globular plants (although a few tend to become slightly cylindrical in shape), covered with numerous ribs which are divided into minute tubercles with close-set areoles. Spines can be few or several, invariably very short. The

*Ferocactus fordii*

plants require a rich cactus compost and careful watering at all times. The soil can be kept just moist even in winter as long as the temperature does not fall below 15°C (60°F). Provide a very bright position where the sun can reach them for 3–4 hours each day; flowers are inclined not to open if conditions are too shaded. They will nevertheless self-pollinate even if closed and, in due course; they will produce viable seeds. Propagation is easy from seeds sown as soon as possible after harvesting.

*F. cataphracta*

First described by E. Dams in 1904 as *Echinocactus*, but later included in its current genus by Britton and Rose. It is a globular plant, 2–4 cm (¾–1½ in) in diameter, dark brownish-red, and usually marked with purplish blotches under the areoles. There are about 15 very low tuberculate ribs with the areoles bearing 5 or more minute yellow spines, closely appressed to the plant body. Flowers are a bright yellow, from the crown of the plant,

*Gymnocalycium bruchii*

and about 4 cm (1½ in) across when fully open. It is native to Paraguay.

### F. asteroides

Discovered in Uruguay and later found in the Rio Grande do Sul region of Brazil, this was described by Werdemann. *F. castanea* is considered a synonym. The plant is similar in shape to a sea urchin. The globular stems are only about 3 cm (1¼ in) in diameter, reddish-brown in colour, with up to 15 regularly spaced ribs. Fine woolly diminutive areoles are set along the slightly rounded ribs, each with 5–7 dark brownish radial spines. The flowers are pale yellow and 3–4.5 cm (1¼–1¾ in) wide.

# GYMNOCALYCIUM

This is one of the most popular genera and possibly includes almost a hundred species and varieties. They are noted for the chin-like clefts generally seen just below the areoles along the tuberculate ribs. The name, established by Pfeiffer in 1845, is from the Greek *gymnos*, meaning naked, and *kalyx*, bud or calyx; it aptly describes the glabrous, smooth flower buds. South America is the habitat of all species; they can be found in open areas exposed to full sun or to whatever weather conditions may prevail. All are globular in shape, a few remain solitary, while the majority develop offsets so as to form groups or clusters. The flowers appear from the uppermost areoles; they are almost wax-like in texture, with a completely spine-free ovary covered with smooth, blunt scales; they appear during late spring and summer. While not all species require identical attention in cultivation, success can be anticipated if the plants are given a bright position and a rich, slightly acid compost with ample gritty sand added to ensure a permeable mix. Water well throughout the growing season, but keep dry from November through until late March, at a minimum temperature of 10°C (50°F). Propagation is easy from seeds sown from January to March; many seedlings will commence flowering after the second year.

### *G. mihanovichii*

This is undoubtedly the best known of the genus, if for no other reason than the red and yellow mutations, which are seen so frequently; these are seedlings developing without chlorophyll, whose only hope of survival is to be grafted on to robust rootstock such as *Trichocereus* or *Hylocereus*. The habitat is Paraguay, and the species was initially included in *Echinocactus* by A.V. Frič and Gürke until transferred to this genus by Britton and Rose. It is a small, greyish-green or brown-reddish-green plant, 3–5 cm (1¼–2 in) in diameter, inclined to be slightly flattened on the top, usually with 8 ribs, deeply furrowed between and set with areoles about 1 cm (⅜ in) apart, with 5–6 yellowish radial spines about 1 cm (⅜ in) long and invariably curved. The flowers are about 4–5 cm (1½–2 in) long, with slender smooth scaly tubes; they are greenish externally with red, yellow or white inner petals. The colour-bodied forms are developed from the var. *friedrichii*.

### *G. gibbosum*

This was named by Pfeiffer and is from southerly regions of Argentina. It can attain 30 cm (12 in) or more in height and 15 cm (6 in) in width. Dark bluish-green in colour, often becoming brownish-green with age, it has 12–19 ribs, straight, tubercled, somewhat rounded with a prominent chin below each areole. The areoles themselves are grey-woolly, bearing 7–10 or more yellowish-brown, spreading radial spines, about 3–4 cm (1¼–1½ in) long, and one or more longer centrals. The flowers are over 6 cm (2½ in) long, with white or reddish lance-shaped petals and white style and stamens. This is one of the most variable species of the genus.

### *G. bruchii*

This is native to Argentina and was so named by C.C. Hosseus. *G. lafaldense* is considered synonymous. It is a densely clustering species, with dark green globular stems, 3–5 cm (1¼–2 in) in diameter, and about 12 tubercled ribs, the chins being almost undiscernible; white areoles carry 9–12 radial spines, tipped yellow, low, bristly and very small, and sometimes one longer central, never more than 6 mm (¼ in) long. The flowers are pale pink with short scaly tubes and are up to 3 cm (1¼ in) long; stamens and style are yellowish-white.

### *G. baldianum*

From Catamarca in Argentina, this is undoubtedly one of the outstanding species of the genus, readily producing deep red flowers; even grown from seeds; plants will begin to flower after two or three years. Stems are dark glossy green, about 7 cm (2¾ in) broad, with 5–7 radial spines from each areole, and subsequently the large flowers, about 5 cm (2 in) long.

# HAAGEOCEREUS

This was established in 1934 by Curt Backeberg and honours Walther Haage, a German authority. The genus contains all columnar species, mainly branching from the base and with most outstanding spination which almost completely covers the branches. There are a large number of species involved, probably well over 30, particularly since *Binghamia*, *Peruvocereus* and certain species from *Loxanthocereus* have been absorbed within the genus. The tubular flowers are nocturnal, some are fragrant. All are of South American origin, from coastal regions to 2500 m (about 7000 ft) altitude in Peru and Chile. Provide a bright, sunny position and a porous fairly rich compost. Water well during the growing season, with 4-weekly feeds of dilute fertilizer, keep the plants dry during dormancy, at a minimum temperature of 10°C (50°F). Propagation is from seeds.

### *H. decumbens*

Found on the hilly slopes of northern Chile and Peru, this was first described by Vaupel as *Cereus decumbens* and later included in *Borzicactus*. The plants grow about 1 m (3 ft 3 in) tall, free-branching, each branch about 6 cm (2½ in) thick, with up to 20 ribs almost hidden by the numerous yellowish spines, about 30 radials and one or more centrals, tending to turn grey with age. Flowers have a tube, 8 cm (3 in) long, brownish externally and white inner petals, about 5 cm (2 in) across at the tips.

### *H. multangularis*

One of the earliest species recorded, it was named *Cactus multangularis* by C.L. von Willdenow in 1813. Since then it has seen many generic changes, having been included in *Cereus*, *Echinocereus*, *Cephalocereus* and *Binghamia*. Ritter made the present transfer. It is more than 1 m (3 ft 3 in) tall and a number of botanical varieties are on record. All are heavily spined, mainly brown or yellowish, and have several ribs, the branches being only up to 10 cm (4 in) thick. The flowers are 8 cm (3 in) long, the inner petals varying from whitish-pink to shades of red, and even sometimes greenish-white. It is native to Peru.

### *H. chosicensis*

One of the finest species, sometimes with white or yellowish spines or, in the var. *rubrospinus*, reddish-brown. It was initially described by Backeberg as *Peruvocereus*. Plants are over 1 m (3 ft 3 in) tall and 10 cm (4 in) in diameter, branching from the base and generally erect in growth. The stems have 14–18 or more ribs, with closely-set areoles bearing numerous spiny bristles, some 2 cm (¾ in) long. Flowers are 6–7 cm (2½–2¾ in) long, with inner petals whitish to varying shades of red, with prominent yellowish style and stamens. It is from Chosica, Peru.

# HARRISIA

A genus established by Nathaniel Britton in 1908 and then involving about 17 species. This number included about five which were later reclassified in *Eriocereus*. There is reason to question the validity of two different genera involving plants so similar in general appearance and most botanical details. At present about 10 species only are named as *Harrisia*, but there seems every likelihood of *Eriocereus* reverting to *Harrisia*, together with *Roseocereus*, in consequence making this one of the larger genera of tall-growing cacti. The generic name acknowledges the Jamaican botanist, James Harris. All are more or less columnar plants, some almost tree-like, while a number tend to trail or scramble among tall scrub and a few become quite shrubby. They are night-flowering plants with large blooms and come principally from certain West Indian islands and Florida. They are of easy culture, demanding much the same conditions as *Eriocereus,* and are readily propagated from either cuttings or seeds. However, successful propagation with both cuttings and seedlings depends upon the maintenance of a temperature of 21–24°C (70–75°F) for at least three months following rooting or germination; a slightly longer period might even be advisable for seedlings.

*Harrisia gracilis*

### H. gracilis

This native to Jamaica was first recorded by Philip Miller in 1768 as *Cereus gracilis*, then incorporated into *Harrisia* by Britton. It is a readily-branching species, to 5 m (16 ft 6 in) or more in height; stems and branches are deep green, about 3 cm (1¼ in) or a little more thick, ascending through scrub or more or less sprawling. There are 9–11 ribs with areoles set about 2 cm (¾ in) apart and bearing 10–16 white, black-tipped spines about 2.5 cm (1 in) long. Flowers appear from the white hairy upper areoles; they are white with yellowish-brown outer segments and about 20 cm (8 in) long. The bright yellow, rounded fruits are most decorative and are about 4 cm (1½ in) in diameter.

### H. eriophora

Pfeiffer named it *Cereus eriophorus* in 1837, and it remained so until transferred to *Harrisia*. This is a branching plant with slender pale green stems and branches that are only about 4 cm (1½ in) thick, yet can grow more than 2 m (6 ft 6 in) high. There are 8–9 closely-set ribs with shallow furrows between, the edges lined with slightly elongated areoles carrying 6–9 dark brown radiating spines, about 4 cm (1½ in) long. Flowers, 12–18 cm (4½–7 in) long, have scaly tubes, pinkish outer segments and white inner petals. A very attractive plant, the fruits of which are edible. It is found in Cuba.

# HATIORA

One of the smaller genera of epiphytic cacti, previously known as *Hariota*, a name established by de Candolle in 1834, and reclassified by Britton and Rose in 1915. It has a close affinity to *Rhipsalis*, to which some species had previously been allocated. The present name is a near-anagram of the previous name which honoured a 16th-century British botanist, Thomas Hariot (*Hariota* had already been adopted for another group of plants). All species consist of small club-shaped segments – some more cylindrical than others, but nevertheless very small, branching in whorls of 2–4. Areoles are scarcely evident, but do appear on each segment and are spineless. The small funnel-shaped flowers are borne terminally, in late winter; they vary in colour, between white, pink and shades of yellow, and have no floral tubes. The genus *Pseudozygocactus* has now been reclassified as *Hatiora*. The plants are easy to grow in good but filtered light. They need an open and porous cactus compost with added leaf-mould and some are suitable for hanging-baskets. Water throughout the year, keeping just moist in winter, when the temperature should not fall below 13°C (55°F). Feed every 4 weeks from May to October with a dilute liquid fertilizer. Propagation is by stem cuttings.

Above left: *Hatiora cylindrica*; above; *Heliocereus speciosus* var. *superbus*

### H. salicornioides

The type species of the genus and undoubtedly the best known *H. salicornioides* was previously recorded by Haworth as *Rhipsalis salicornioides*. It is a small bushy plant, more or less erect, the many branches often attaining 40 cm (16 in) in height; they are composed of small bottle-shaped segments, each 1–2 cm ($\frac{3}{8}$–$\frac{3}{4}$ in) long. Areoles have short whitish bristles and flowers, approximately 12 mm ($\frac{1}{2}$ in) long, more or less funnel-shaped and deep yellow in colour, orange-yellow on the exterior. The stamens are reddish; and both the style and stigma lobes are white. *Hatiora bambusoides* is very similar, but the segments are longer and stouter, and the flowers are generally orange. Both the species are from the Rio de Janeiro area of Brazil.

### H. herminiae

Discovered in Brazil in 1942, this was first named by Campos Porto and Castellanos as a *Hariota*. The small joints are almost cylindrical, developing by whorls into small bushy plants. Flowers are deep pink and borne from the small terminal areoles; fruits are bright pale green.

### H. epiphylloides

Also discovered in 1942 and again placed in *Hariota*. However, a new genus *Pseudozygocactus* was established by Backeberg to contain this plant and its var. *bradei* until it was merged into *Hatiora* in 1984. The stem segments are flattish, about 2.5 cm (1 in) long and 1 cm ($\frac{3}{8}$ in) wide, in some ways resembling *Rhipsalidopsis rosea*. Flowers appear at the tips of the segments, bright yellow in colour. *H. epiphylloides* var. *bradei* has small, flat, club-shaped joints and pale yellow flowers. Both species and variety are native to Brazil.

### H. cylindrica

From the Rio de Janeiro district of Brazil, this is something of a controversial species. It has been placed as a synonym of a *Rhipsalis* species to which it seems to have slight resemblance. It is a bushy plant with numerous cylindrical joints, each about 3 cm ($1\frac{1}{4}$ in) long, dull green in colour and bearing more or less terminal golden-yellow or orange-yellow trumpet-like flowers.

# HELIOCEREUS

This genus constitutes a group of beautiful flowering cacti. The name is from the Greek, meaning sun-cactus, and the brilliance of the flowers certainly supports that. The name was first erected by Berger as a sub-section of the then genus *Cereus* and was given generic status by Britton and Rose in 1909. The growth differs considerably from one species to another; it is mainly erect but rather soft and fleshy so that the stems tend to droop. They are more or less angular or prominently ribbed, with large, prominent areoles bearing spines and usually just one flower to an areole. The plants are summer flowering and diurnal. Six species are recorded plus a few varieties. They grow well in either full sun or partly shaded positions; the latter seems to be preferable, particularly as there are epiphytes among the species. They require an acid soil with sufficient gritty sand to make the mixture really porous. Water regularly from April to October and keep only barely moist in winter. Maintain the temperature at a minimum of 10°C (50°F) or higher if possible. Propagation is by cuttings in summer. *Heliocereus* species have played their part in the production of many of the fine cultivars of *Epiphyllum*, the flower colour being particularly apparent in such well-known hybrids as 'Jenkinsonii' and 'Ackermannii'.

### H. speciosus

Initially termed *Cereus speciosus* by Cavanilles in 1803, this became the type species of *Heliocereus*. It is found in Central Mexico, towards Mexico City. The stems are up to 1 m (3 ft 3 in) long, mostly erect, but sometimes becoming semi-pendent; they are 4-angled, with acute ribs which are unevenly serrated. The growing tips of the branches are reddish-pink at first, but later become deep green. Areoles are set at intervals of 1–3 cm ($\frac{3}{8}$–$1\frac{1}{4}$ in) along the ribs; they are brown in colour, and bear 5–8 brownish spines which gradually multiply in number, and are about 1.5 cm ($\frac{5}{8}$ in) long. Flowers are rich scarlet, about 12–15 cm ($4\frac{1}{2}$–6 in) long, with an 8 cm (3 in) long green tube. The variety *superbus* has very large carmine-red flowers with a metallic blue sheen on the inner petals. Other varieties include *amecamensis*, which once enjoyed generic status; it has large whitish flowers, 12 cm ($4\frac{1}{2}$ in) in diameter. The variety *elegantissimus* has stems 20 cm (8 in) long, angled with undulating margins, and scarlet flowers about 12 cm ($4\frac{1}{2}$ in) across.

### H. cinnabarinus

Native to Guatemala and brought into this genus by Britton and Rose after having been first described by F. Eichlam in 1910 as *Cereus*. It has very slender branches of spreading habit, rarely more than 1.5 cm ($\frac{5}{8}$ in) thick, with 3–4 ribs, and areoles bearing about 10 bristly spines 8 mm ($\frac{5}{16}$ in) long. Flowers are cinnabar-red, almost wax-like, 9 cm ($3\frac{1}{2}$ in) long and about 5 cm (2 in) across. Style and stamens are white below and pinkish-purple above; the stigma is white.

### H. schrankii

Originally *Cereus schrankii*, it is known only from the area of Zimapan in Mexico. It has 4-angled dull green stems, 2–3 cm ($\frac{3}{4}$–$1\frac{1}{4}$ in) thick, with serrated edges, the growing tips of the stems being reddish. The areoles bear 7 or more whitish spines, each about 1 cm ($\frac{3}{8}$ in) long, and flowers of deep scarlet often suffused with blue at the base of the inner petals. They are about 14 cm ($5\frac{1}{2}$ in) long, with short greenish tubes, and 8–9 cm ($3\frac{1}{2}$–$3\frac{3}{4}$ in) wide at the tips. Stamens are numerous, white and bluish-red; the style exceeds the stamens and is carmine-red with white base and red stigma lobes tipped yellow.

More recent introductions of this genus have revealed a close affinity with species of *Nopalxochia*, although there are obvious differences in the shape of the stems. Two in particular are of considerable interest. *H. aurantiacus*, discovered by A.H. Heller and named by Kimnach, whose specific title aptly describes the brilliant orange-red colour of the flowers, has long, angled but slender stems, up to 1 m (3 ft 3 in) long, and is very much an epiphyte. It is native to Nicaragua near the town of Jinotega. *H. luzmariae*, so named by L. Scheinvar in 1985, is from Oaxaca and Jalisco in southern Mexico. This is an epiphyte, in many ways resembling *H. schrankii*. The purplish-red flowers have a velvety metallic suffusion and appear during the day; they are about 12 cm ($4\frac{1}{2}$ in) long and wide, borne on short curved tubes.

# HYLOCEREUS

This is a genus of some 24 species, all of them epiphytic. Its present status was established by Britton and Rose in 1909, and all its species are climbing, clambering plants, of forest habitats. The name emphasizes this, the Greek word *hylos* meaning forest. The majority are very similar in general habit as well as stem formation; stems and branches, varying from 3 to 5, are angular in shape and almost wing-like. Long aerial roots appear at intervals along the branches, with which the plants climb trees or grip the rocky terrain below. The flowers are all nocturnal and begin to appear in spring; they are among the largest of the Cactaceae. Their habitats extend from Mexico throughout much of Central America and the West Indies, and the more northerly regions of South America. All the species are easy to grow, given a position with filtered light and a proprietary cactus compost with added leaf-mould. Water freely during the growing season and give a dilute liquid feed every three or four weeks; in winter maintain a minimum temperature of 10°C (50°F), with the compost kept just moist. Propagate from stem cuttings in summer.

### H. undatus

The best known of the genus, this was previously recorded by Haworth as *Cereus undatus* in 1830 and subse-

*Heliocereus speciosus* var. *amecamensis*

quently reclassified under the present name in 1918. It is found in many of the West Indian islands, and is almost naturalized in many tropical New World countries. The stems are mainly three-angled with pronounced undulate margins, which become very hard and horny in maturity. The areoles bear one to three small, dark brown spines and flowers up to 30 cm (1 ft) long; the recurved back petals are yellowish-green and the broad, erect inner petals pure white; style, stamens and stigma lobes are all cream-coloured.

### H. napoleonis

This species, whose true habitat was for many years uncertain, has been located on St Vincent in the West Indies. The first mention of it was in Curtis's *Botanical Magazine* in 1836 with the name *Cereus napoleonis*; it was transferred to *Hylocereus* by Britton and Rose in 1909. The branches are three-angled, the areoles quite closely set and bearing 4–5 stiff, fairly long spines. The flowers are about 20 cm (8 in) long, the inner petals pure white and the outer yellowish-cream.

### H. guatemalensis

Found only in the rain-forests of Guatemala, this was first described by Eichlam as *Cereus trigonus*

*Hylocereus calcaratus*

*guatemalensis*. It has been widely used by Japanese horticulturalists for grafting stock. The stems are long, three-angled and only infrequently jointed; the margins are horny and slightly undulating, areoles closely set with two or three short, dark brownish spines. The flowers are approximately 30 cm (1 ft) long, the outer petals are pinkish-rose, while the inner pure white, and style and stigma lobes are yellow.

Two species are oustanding, with individual characteristics. *H. stenopterus* is, along with *H. extensus*, the most slender-stemmed species of the genus. Both were originally ascribed to the genus *Cereus*. *H. stenopterus*, a Costa Rican species, has the unique distinction of producing reddish-purple flowers, which are enhanced by white style, stamens and stigma lobes. Another, *H. calcaratus*, also from Costa Rica, has very different stem and branch growth; it is three-winged, but the margins possess many prominent lobes. The areoles are small, appearing in the axil of each lobe. The attractive flowers are large, about 20 cm (8 in) or more long; the outer petals are creamy-yellow and widely spreading, the inner ones are pure white and are, embellished by numerous creamy-yellow stamens and a long protruding style of similar colour.

# JASMINOCEREUS

A genus that has captivated the imagination of cactus enthusiasts, if for no other reason than the isolated habitat of the Galapagos Islands. It was established by Britton and Rose in 1920 for just a single species – and remains monotypic. The name describes the fragrance of the nocturnal flowers, which resembles that of *Jasminum*, the popular shrub jasmine. Plants are columnar in habit, often forming tree-like proportions and branching freely at the top. Though rare in cultivation the plants are not difficult to grow successfully as long as a rich, very open compost is provided. Warmth is another consideration; temperatures should be kept above 15°C (60°F) throughout the year. Avoid too high humidity and provide as bright a position as possible. Water in moderation from April through to late September, with a dilute liquid fertilizer every four weeks; in winter give occasional waterings with tepid water, enough to ensure that the soil does not dry out completely but is kept barely moist. Propagation can be achieved by cuttings or seeds.

### J. galapagensis

Was described by Weber as *Cereus galapagensis* in 1899. It comes from St Charles Island and can also be found in other islands of the Galapagos group. History tells us that it was Charles Darwin who first located the plant in 1835. A tall species, in habitat more than 7 m (23 ft) high, with a thick cylindrical trunk 30 cm (1 ft) in diameter. The branches are much jointed and about 15 cm (6 in) wide; these developing from about halfway up the trunk to the top. They have 15–18 ribs, very low set with brown-felted areoles densely arrayed along the edges. Each areole carries about 10 spines, very slender and 1–8 cm ($\frac{3}{8}$–3 in) in length. The sweetly scented flowers are red or reddish-brown, sometimes with indistinct yellow stripes longitudinally, and 5–10 cm (2–4 in) long with scaly, sometimes woolly tubes. Fruits are greenish, about 5 cm (2 in) long and 4 cm ($1\frac{1}{2}$ in) wide, and supposedly edible. Other names, specific and varietal have been ascribed to this species, including *J. howellii* and var. *delicatus, J. sclerocarpus*, which from early on, when it was known as *Cereus sclerocarpus*, was presumed synonymous; *J. thouarsii* and var. *chathamensis*, all seemingly associated with different islands but all indistinguishable from *J. galapagensis*.

# LEOCEREUS

This genus was raised by Britton and Rose in 1920 and contains five Brazilian species. The name recognizes a former Director of Rio de Janeiro Botanic Gardens, Pacheco Leão. They are bushy plants of somewhat climbing habit, with very slender stems, which may reach to 2 m (6 ft 6 in) in length. There are several ribs with many spines and nocturnal flowers. Fruits are quite small and contain black seeds. The species are not common in cultivation, although with due care they can be grown very successfully. A fairly rich cactus compost, which should be thoroughly free-draining, is essential and so is a very bright position though not in full sun. Water in moderation from April to October, and feed every 3–4 weeks throughout this period. Keep the plants fairly dry throughout the winter months and at a temperature of 13°C (55°F) as a minimum, with an occasional light watering so as just to moisten the compost. Propagation is by seeds in late winter and early spring.

### L. bahiensis

The type species, it comes from the state of São Paulo. The stems are erect or clambering, sometimes branching, rarely more than 1 m (3 ft 3 in) long and only 1.5 cm ($\frac{5}{8}$ in) wide, with 12–14 low ribs. The whitish areoles are closely set and bear numerous yellowish radial spines and a few centrals, these often to 3 cm ($1\frac{1}{4}$ in) long, all mostly spreading. Flowers are about 4 cm ($1\frac{1}{2}$ in) long, the tubes densely woolly and scaly and opening to small bell-shaped white blooms with very short inner petals.

### L. glaziovii

Described by Schumann in 1890 as *Cereus glaziovii*, this is found in Minas Gerais. The stems are very slender, to 2 cm ($\frac{3}{4}$ in) thick, frequently branching. There are 12, more or less straight low ribs with slightly elongating areoles bearing up to 30 brownish, rather short spines not exceeding 2.5 cm (1 in) in length. The funnel-shaped flowers are borne from near the tops of the stems; they are 8 cm (3 in) long, with greenish outer segments and white inner petals. The oval fruits are about 2 cm ($\frac{3}{4}$ in) long.

# LEPISMIUM

This group of plants is of epiphytic habit, sometimes saxicolous (i.e., growing on rocks). Much confusion surrounds the genus and the correct allocation of species because of their close similarities with *Rhipsalis, Pfeiffera* and *Hatiora*. The genus was established in 1835 by Ludwig Pfeiffer for just one species, *Lepismium commune* (now *L. cruciforme*). The generic name is taken from the Greek *lepis*, meaning a scale, and refers to the small scales set beneath the areoles. At a much later date Backeberg enlarged the scope of characteristics to include species in which the ovary was sunk into the stems during the flowering period, and in this way differed from species of *Rhipsalis*. This resulted in the comparatively few species then classified as *Lepismium* being increased, according to some authorities, to include 15 or more species, a number of these having been transferred from *Rhipsalis*. Initially, the species had mostly flat, almost leaf-like branches or were angled or three-winged; currently the majority, chiefly those moved from *Rhipsalis*, have more or less cylindrical stems, at least in cross-section. One or several flowers are borne from each areole in early spring; they are white or pink in colour, followed by small berry-like fruits.

All species, of South American origin, are of easy culture; many are ideally suited for hanging-basket culture where the elongated branches can be allowed to drape elegantly round the container. A rich compost containing thoroughly decomposed humus is very important; watering is necessary more or less throughout the year, freely in summer, and sufficient to avoid the roots drying out in winter. Maintain a minimum temperature of 10°C (50°F). Feeding at two- or three-week intervals is helpful, best from when flower buds begin to form until after the flowers have faded and the fruits begin to appear. Propagation is by cuttings or seeds sown in late winter or early spring.

### L. cruciforme

This variable species from Brazil, Paraguay and Argentina has a number of botanically recognized vari-

*Lepismium cruciforme*

pearing at the top of each angle; they are small, slightly woolly and occasionally with one to three very fine bristles, more so on young growth. The flowers, about 2 cm ($\frac{3}{4}$ in) long, are white, and the fruits, white at first, later become reddish.

# LEPTOCEREUS

This generic name was established by Britton and Rose in 1909, the plant having previously been classed as a sub-genus of *Cereus*. The name is from the Greek *leptos*, meaning thin, and applies in particular to the slender stems and branches. There is a closely allied genus, *Neoabbottia*, which is now considered synonymous. All species are native to the West Indies, principally Cuba, Haiti and Puerto Rico. They are creeping or clambering in habit, the thin stems often forming quite thick shrubby clumps. Stems have only few ribs, with areoles bearing very fine sharp spines and small diurnal, bell-shaped flowers borne laterally. The plants are uncommon in cultivation; they require a very bright position, though not necessarily in full sun but not too shaded. Warmth is a primary need, the higher the temperature, the better, and in winter anything below 15°C (60°F) can cause problems. A rich compost is advised, with sufficient added sand to ensure good drainage, and limestone chippings. Water freely from April to October; thereafter, between November and March, an occasional light misting with tepid water is beneficial. Propagation is from cuttings or seeds.

eties. It is the type species, which had to forego its earlier name of *L. commune* because Velloza had, in 1825, named the same plant *Cactus cruciformis* and his title took precedence. A creeping, trailing species, usually saxicolous, with flattened branches, sometimes angled, often 30 cm (1 ft) or more long and 2 cm ($\frac{3}{4}$ in) wide. Where it grows epiphytically on trees it spreads by means of aerial roots. The stems are dark green, sometimes quite reddish, the margins with crenations where the small areoles occur. There are no spines as such, but occasionally a few very fine hair-like bristles. White or reddish flowers, about 1.5 cm ($\frac{5}{8}$ in) long, are borne singly or several to an areole. Fruits are rounded, about 1 cm ($\frac{3}{8}$ in) in diameter and reddish or purplish. The several different forms include var. *cavernosum*, var. *myosurus*, var. *anceps* and var. *radicans*.

### L. paradoxum

From the São Paulo region of Brazil, this is a very free-branching species, named by J. Salm-Reifferscheid-Dyck, with elongated, twisted stems which reach 50 cm (20 in) or more; frequently, the stems branch in whorls which adds fascination to a rather lovely epiphyte. The branches are somewhat three-angled, the areoles ap-

### L. assurgens

The type species was earlier described, by C. Wright in 1866, as *Cereus assurgens*. It is a tall-growing, much-branching plant from Cuba, of clambering habit and often reaching 3 m (10 ft) in height; the branches are about 3 cm ($1\frac{1}{4}$ in) thick, with 4 pronounced ribs and areoles set well apart, bearing about 16 needle-like radial spines and four central spines, all yellowish-brown and 2–8 cm ($\frac{3}{4}$–3 in) in length. The flowers are bell-shaped, about 4 cm ($1\frac{1}{2}$ in) long, with pink outer segments and bright yellow inner petals, opening to about 2.5 cm (1 in) across.

### L. maxonii

Described by Britton and Rose and named after the discoverer of the plant, William R. Maxon, this is a branching plant, about 1.5 m (5 ft) high, the branches either semi-erect or slightly drooping. There are 5–7 ribs, with areoles set 2 cm ($\frac{3}{4}$ in) apart and bearing approximately 20 sharp brownish-yellow spines, 3 cm ($1\frac{1}{4}$ in) long. The flowers, which can be up to 6 cm ($2\frac{1}{2}$ in) in length, are yellowish-green in colour and have floral tubes densely covered with yellow spines. It is native to Cuba.

# LEUCHTENBERGIA

This genus was named by William J. Hooker in 1848 for Eugène de Beauharnais, Duke of Leuchtenberg and Prince of Eichstädt, a French statesman and son of Empress Josephine. It contains just a single species which is native to Hidalgo, San Luis Potosí, Coahuila, Guanajuato and Zacatecas in central and north Mexico. No other cactus even remotely resembles this unusual plant, which has the appearance of a stunted *Agave*, with only a short section of the stem growth being visible; it grows from a fleshy rootstock in the form of a large single or branched taproot. For successful culture it is essential to provide a warm site in full sun; even in winter the temperature should not be allowed to drop below 10°C (50°F). Excellent drainage is important. Use a proprietary cactus compost, with sharp sand added, as well as limestone chippings to simulate the soil conditions of the natural habitat. Water carefully at all times, letting the plants dry out between applications in spring and summer, and in winter keeping them bone dry. Give established plants an occasional feed during the growing season. Propagation is from seeds only.

## L. principis

Plants reach about 70 cm (28 in) high at maturity, but they are extremely slow-growing and take many years to reach this height; they are also known to branch. The main feature being the tubercles, which are bluish-green, 10–13 cm (4–5 in) long, three-angled and more or less erect, with terminal clusters of thin, papery spines; these consist of 8–14 radials, flat and twisted and about 10 cm (4 in) long, and one or two very similar centrals, often slightly longer. The flowers are long-lasting, shiny yellow and rather funnel-shaped, about 10 cm (4 in) across when fully open; they arise from areoles set just below the tips of young tubercles. Stamens, style and stigma lobes are yellow and exceed the flower petals.

# LOBIVIA

A well-known group of cacti that particularly attracts the enthusiast because of the extensive range of colours displayed in the flowers. The generic name is an anagram of Bolivia, where a considerable number of the species originate. It was established by Britton and Rose in 1922, naming as the type species a plant previously designated by Hooker as *Echinocactus pentlandii*. It bears flowers of many colours from golden-yellow to red and purple. A few years ago the popular peanut cactus, *Chamaecereus*, was reclassified as belonging to this genus, as also were the genera *Acantholobivia* and *Cinnabarina*. The true status of *Lobivia* is currently undergoing consideration by taxonomists, the theory being that there is little to differentiate between *Lobivia* and certain species included in *Echinopsis*, *Trichocereus*, *Soehrensia* and others. If an amalgamation of these genera takes place, all species of *Lobivia* could well be referred to *Echinopsis*, this being the earlier established name.

Plants vary considerably in shape and spine formation, being mainly globular or short-cylindrical, a number remaining solitary while others develop clusters. The flowers are all diurnal. Geographically, Lobivias as at present understood are found not only in Bolivia, but also in Argentina and Peru, where they are located in the Andes. They thrive in a bright, sunny position, at temperatures as low as 7°C (45°F) in winter as long as they are kept dry; higher temperatures in spring and summer help to support good growth and successful flowering. Use any commercial cactus compost, and feed occasionally from April to September. During summer, water thoroughly as the soil dries out. Propagation is by offsets removed during spring and summer or seeds sown between January and March.

## L. pentlandii

First included in *Echinocactus*, it has a great number of synonyms, the majority bearing the generic name of *Echinopsis*, a fact which gives added force to the argument for the amalgamation of the two genera. A most variable species, widely distributed in the wild, around Puno in Peru and northerly parts of Bolivia. It bears flowers from the sides of the stems, in colours of yellow, orange, pink and red, often beautifully marked with other colourings. Plants can be either single and more or less globular in shape, or clustering in small groups. They have 10–20 ribs, which are deeply crenate, with radial spines, varying in number from mainly 5–6, to as many as 15, and 1–9 centrals, 3–9 cm ($1\frac{1}{4}$–$3\frac{1}{2}$ in) long. The flowers are truly exceptional, being 3–8 cm ($1\frac{1}{4}$–3 in) in length.

## L. boliviensis

Found by Rose on the dry hillsides at Oruro in Bolivia, it is a clustering species with 6–10 in a group, each stem oval or globular and 10 cm (4 in) wide; it has about 20 tuberculate, undulating ribs, the areoles set 1 cm ($\frac{3}{8}$ in) apart and bearing 6–8 slender spines, 6–9 cm ($2\frac{1}{2}$–$3\frac{1}{2}$ in) long and more or less upward-pointing. Flowers are deep orange-yellow. A rather unusual species, possessing a thick fleshy rootstock.

## L. backebergii

First named by Werdemann as an *Echinopsis*, honouring Curt Backeberg with the specific name; Backeberg himself later transferred it to *Lobivia*. It is a Bolivian species from high-mountain areas above La Paz. The stems are

*Lobivia boliviensis*

either solitary or in clusters, oval in shape and about 5 cm (2 in) in diameter. In this, and other respects, the species can be variable, resulting in varieties or forms being recorded. There are 12–15 spirally-arranged notched ribs with rather woolly areoles bearing 3–8 brown to greyish radial spines, slender, often curved, and 1.2–5 cm ($\frac{1}{2}$–2 in) or more in length. Flowers are deep carmine, about 5 cm (2 in) long, sometimes with a paler red or glossy, bluish-sheened throat.

## L. densispina

From the Jujuy region of Argentina, this is something of a conundrum plant, which, due to the interpretations given of the various characteristics by different botanists, make it a difficult plant to describe in detail. The specific name was raised by Werdemann then 're-phrased' by Backeberg. It has a fleshy root system like a taproot and stems that are dark purplish-green in colour, more or less cylindrical in shape. There are 8–10

very clearly defined ribs, the small areoles bearing numerous tiny radial spines and 4–7 centrals, brownish-yellow and set comb-like, though sometimes less formal. Flowers as well as spination can vary according to the variety; in var. *densipina* the flowers are pale yellow or crimson, often purplish-red. The var. *rebutioides*, which has had a confusing history at the hands of botanists, has only few spines, rarely more than 9 pale whitish radials and one or two centrals; the flowers are in pale yellow to reddish shades. Another form, var. *sublimiflora*, which once enjoyed specific status, has dark greenish-purplish stems with spines set comb-like, and flowers in a variety of bright colours – yellow, orange, pink and red.

## L. silvestrii

The popular peanut cactus was originally named *Cereus silvestrii* by Carlos Spegazzini, then classified by Britton and Rose under a new generic name, *Chamaecereus*, in 1922; Rowley later placed in in *Lobivia*. Many interesting hybrids have been raised by cross-pollinating with other

*Lobivia* species. It comes from the mountainous regions of Salta and Tucumán in Argentina, and is a trailing, prostrate species, with small joints, rarely more than 6 cm (2½ in) long and 12 mm (½ in) in diameter; with 6–9 low straight ribs, the areoles having 10–15 small bristly whitish spines. The flowers, which are vermilion, are 2 cm (¾ in) wide and 5–7 cm (2–2¾ in) long. *Lobivia sylvestrii* has proved to be an almost hardy plant in many parts of Europe including Britain, and elsewhere, but to take advantage of this, plants must be grown in well-drained soil and given protection from heavy rains in winter.

### L. wrightiana
Named by Backeberg and native to Peru and possibly Chile, this is an outstanding species. It grows from a taproot, sometimes multiple-branched. Plants are solitary or, rarely, clustering, globular or slightly elongated, with 12–17 spirally arranged, notched ribs; the yellow-brown areoles bear 6–10 radials and one central spine, the latter being decidedly long and twisted and up to 7 cm (2¾ in) in length, while the others are only 3 cm (1¼ in) in length. The flowers are a truly beautiful pink, which becomes paler towards the throat. They are more than 4 cm (1½ in) long and the same wide, and their attraction is emphasized by the display of yellow stamens.

# LOPHOCEREUS

This very small genus of columnar plants was established in 1909 by Britton and Rose. The name is from the Greek *lophos*, meaning crest, and obviously refers to the long bristly spines, especially those towards the tips of the stems. The plants are erect or semi-erect in habit, generally producing branches from the base. The genus is closely linked with *Pachycereus*, and is likely to be merged with it eventually, although the loss of a well-known generic name will be regretted. All the species are native to northern Mexico, Baja California and southern Arizona. They are easy in cultivation; a bright position is an advantage, although in habitat the plants frequently associate themselves with low trees and scrub. Prolonged hot sun could possibly spoil the appearance of the stems. Provide an ordinary cactus compost, but add limestone chippings to meet the natural requirements, and perhaps grit to make certain that the mixture is porous. Water should be given freely from April through to October, but keep the plants, during dormancy, at a minimum temperature of 10°C (50°F). Feed with a weak liquid fertilizer every 3–4 weeks throughout the growing season. Propagate from cuttings in summer, or from seeds in spring.

*Lophocereus schottii*

### *L. schottii*

This, the best known and most popular of the species, was first named by Engelmann in 1856 as *Cereus schottii* and was brought into the present genus as the type species of 1909. A tall plant with long branches ascending to 5 m (16 ft 6 in) or more, about 6 cm (2½ in) thick and greyish-green in colour. There are 5–7 ribs, the edges bearing large white woolly areoles set fairly close together and carrying five to seven dark greyish spines. In maturity the tips of the branches become somewhat pale purple and long hairy bristles develop in the form of a pseudocephalium; flowers appear from these tufted areas. Each nocturnal flower is about 4 cm (1½ in) long, with a short tube, greenish externally, and reddish inner petals with prominent white stamens. A monstrose form occasionally occurs in the wild, more so with plants exposed to the sun. Monstrose plants are almost devoid of spines and ribs and consist of a more or less cylindrical stem, often twisted, almost gnarled; its common name is totem-pole cactus.

# LOPHOPHORA

This small genus of possibly only three species was established by J.M. Coulter in 1894. The name is from the Greek *lophos*, meaning crest, and *phorein*, to carry; it seemingly refers to the tufts of hairs borne on the areoles. Its common name is the peyote cactus and it is said to contain a potent narcotic which causes hallucinations; it plays an important role in many native Indian ceremonies and dances. The plants are all native to USA (Texas and New Mexico) through to central parts of Mexico; in the wild, they tend to sink into the ground during the hot season so that only their greyish surface can be seen. *Lophophora* are globular plants, with a flattened bluish-green or greyish surface. When first recorded by Lemaire the one species known was placed in *Echinocactus*; 40 years later it was classified in the newly established genus *Anhalonium*. In 1891, it was transferred by Coulter to *Mammillaria*, just three years prior to the erection of the genus recognized today. In cultivation plants require a very sandy compost, the higher the mineral content, the better. Temperatures are best maintained at a minimum of 10°C (50°F) in winter and a really sunny position is essential. Water moderately throughout the growing and flowering season, but keep the plants completely dry during dormancy. Propagate from seeds in late winter and early spring.

### *L. williamsii*

This is the type species. It has a wide distribution and is fairly abundant in parts of central Mexico. It has a long,

*Lophophora williamsii*

thick taproot 10–15 cm (4–6 in) in length; the plant body is about 7–8 cm (2¾–3 in) broad, with 7–10 shallow ribs indistinctly tubercled. Areoles are large with a tuft of whitish hairs, or wool. Flowers appear from the newer areoles in the crown of the plant; they are about 2.5 cm (1 in) wide, white or pinkish, usually with a darker median line. Stamens and style are whitish, stigma lobes yellowish or pale red. This species sprouts growths to form groups – often 10 or more offsets develop.

### L. echinata

Both this and its variety *diffusa* are similar to the above, but flowers are pure white, followed by pale reddish fruit. It is native to Texas.

### L. lutea

This is recorded by Backeberg, but no habitat is given. It is purported to have wrinkled ribs and yellowish-white flowers. It would appear to be similar to another recorded species, *L. ziegleri* from Mexico, said to be very uncommon in cultivation. These two species are probably forms of *L. williamsii*.

# MAIHUENIA

A very small genus of fascinating dwarf cacti from Chile and Argentina. The name was established by R.A. Phil-ippi in 1883 being derived from the local name of the type species, *maihuen*. Certain of the five species were previously included in *Opuntia* with which there is a close affinity, as there is with *Pereskia*, but *Maihuenia* differs in having no glochids. Plants have short cylindrical stem segments, very similar to some of the dwarf *Opuntia* species. They also have small rounded leaves, which persist. Another feature, uncommon in the Cactaceae, is the lack of flower tube. Most of the species are still considered rare in cultivation, yet they are not difficult to grow. They all are high-altitude plants, and in consequence most of them can prove winter-hardy in much of Europe, but the importance of giving them a really porous compost cannot be over-emphasized. Given good drainage and a measure of protection from torrential or persistent rain during the winter months, their degree of hardiness is remarkable. However, provide as bright and sunny a position as possible throughout the year, indoors or out, and endeavour to keep the soil as dry as possible during dormancy. Propagate by seed in early spring or by cuttings in summer.

### M. poeppigii

Originally described by C. Friedrich Otto as an *Opuntia*, this later became the type species for *Maihuenia*. It comes

*Maihuenia poeppigii*

from the high Andean mountains of Chile and is particularly resistant to extreme temperatures, even below freezing. The stems are about 6 cm (2½ in) long and a little over 1 cm (⅜ in) in diameter, bearing a few soft spines from the areoles. Small green leaves also develop, about 4 mm (⅛ in) long and persistent. Flowers are about 3 cm (1¼ in) long, yellow and borne terminally. Fruits are about 5 cm (2 in) long, and oblong in shape.

## *M. valentinii*

This comes from southwestern Argentina in the district of Chubut and was described by Spegazzini in 1902. It is a more shrubby species and taller in growth, reaching 20 cm (8 in) in height; the stems are similar but longer than those of *M. poeppigii*. The flowers are white, with pinkish-red sepals; the style and stamens are whitish, and the 5 short stigma lobes purple. Another tall-growing species, *M. tehuelches*, can sometimes be even taller and somewhat branched. It comes from southwestern parts of Argentina and has creamy-white flowers, about 4 cm (1½ in) wide, from the tips of the branches.

# MAMMILLARIA

This is one of the largest and most popular of all genera in the Cactaceae; many specific names have been addressed to *Mammillaria* through the years, and now about 170 names are considered authentic. The generic name is from the Latin *mammilla*, meaning nipple, and this refers to the tubercles that cover the bodies of all species instead of the ribs that are a characteristic of most cacti. The genus was established by Haworth in 1812 only to be replaced by *Neomammillaria* when Britton and Rose in 1923 realized that *Mammillaria* was already in use for species of *Algae*. However, the original name is again generally accepted. The majority of species are native to Mexico, although a number are found in the USA, West Indies, South America and certain Central American countries. Several genera have merged with *Mammillaria*, such as *Solisia*, *Dolichothele*, *Cochemiea*, *Oehmea*, *Krainzia* and others; while there were undoubtedly many similarities which justified the amalgamation, equally so were there obvious differences. In consequence, the genus is now divided into sub-genera, sections and series so as better to define the peculiarities. A specialist Mammillaria Society exists in Great Britain for the precise purpose of gaining a better understanding of these plants, and membership can prove advantageous to those who have a particular interest in this direction.

Mammillarias are mainly globular, some ultimately becoming slightly elongated. A few remain solitary, but many others form offsets very freely and spread to form large cushions. Yet others are dichotomous, when the plant body divides to form two branches. Tubercles cover the plants in spiralling rows, and spines develop from the tips where the areoles are situated. Flowers appear from the axils at the point where areole and axil merge, almost suggesting an areole with two growing points, the lower one for spines, the upper for flowers. The majority of species are of easy culture. In general a proprietary cactus compost is suitable, although there are those that may need the addition of limestone chippings so as to meet their material requirements – this applies particularly to those with distinctive white spination, such as *M. plumosa*. All should be provided with a really bright position; water freely throughout the growing season with added fertilizer every three or four weeks. Keep the plants totally dry in winter, at a minimum temperature of 7°C (45°F). Propagation is relatively easy from seeds, or by careful removal of the offsets.

*Mammillaria elongata*

## *M. elongata*

One of the best-known species, described by de Candolle in 1828. It is included in the sub-genus *Mammillaria*, series *Leptocladodae*, and comes from Hidalgo in Mexico. The species is a free-clustering plant of many more or less erect stems, cylindrical in shape and rarely more than 10 cm (4 in) long and 3 cm (1¼ in) thick, covered with numerous small tubercles. Areoles are slightly woolly and carry 15–20 radial spines and sometimes just one central spine; these are only about 1 cm (⅜ in) long and can vary in colour from white to yellow, or shades of brown and reddish-brown (at one time, they all had varietal status). Flowers appear from the side axils and are about 1.5 cm (⅝ in) long, whitish or pale yellowish, sometimes with a darker red central line on the petals. Stamens, style and stigma lobes are white. Pink fruits turn red and contain many light brown seeds.

### M. dioica

This is in the same sub-genus and the series *Ancistracanthae*. It was named by K. Brandegee in 1897 and is native to southern California and Baja. It is a cylindrical plant about 25 cm (10 in) high, either clustering or remaining solitary, and rather bluish-green in colour. Each areole carries 11–20 radial spines, whitish and tipped reddish or brown, and one to four dark brown centrals, one of which is hooked. Flowers are formed in a ring around the crown. The colour of the flowers can vary; they are occasionally a yellowish-white colour with a reddish-purple midrib, or sometimes they are all pink.

*Mammillaria zephyranthoides*

### M. zephyranthoides

Belonging to the same series *Ancistracanthae*, this comes from high altitudes in Oaxaca, Mexico. It was first described by Scheidweiler in 1841. A solitary species, globular and with tubercles to 2.5 cm (1 in) long which are tipped with areoles each bearing 12–18 whitish, hair-like spines about 1 cm ($\frac{3}{8}$ in) long and, usually, one larger, brown-yellow hooked central spine (in rare instances two central spines appear). Flowers are whitish with a red central median line and about 4 cm (1$\frac{1}{2}$ in) long and wide.

### M. angelensis

This has a close affinity with *M. dioica*. Described by Craig in 1945, it is found in Baja California and on Angel de la Guarda Island, from which it takes its name. Stems are 15 cm (6 in) high, either solitary or clustering, the areoles with up to 16 radial and 3–4 central spines, all 1 cm ($\frac{3}{8}$ in) or more long. Flowers are creamy-white, with pink central lines on the sepals.

### M. plumosa

One of the choicest and most beautiful of the genus. It was described by Weber in 1898 and is included in the series *Lasiacanthae*. It is found in Coahuila, Mexico, on limestone hillsides, often literally affixed to the rock itself as can be seen between Saltillo and Monterey. Definitely a clustering plant, with dense woolly axils, soft feathery white spines, frequently up to 40 from each areole, all radials, no centrals. The whitish or yellowish flowers scarcely protrude beyond the woolly surface and are only about 1.5 cm ($\frac{5}{8}$ in) long and wide. Pink-purple fruits contain black seeds. This lovely species requires very careful watering.

### M. schiedeana

A high-altitude plant from Puente de Dios, Hidalgo, in Mexico, it is very close to *M. plumosa*. It has white woolly axils with numerous yellowish, fine spines – all radials – and hairs from each areole. Flowers appear late in the season; they are creamy-white and about 1.5 cm ($\frac{5}{8}$ in) long, with whitish filaments and style and 4 stigma lobes. It was named by C.G. Ehrenberg in 1838.

### M. klissingiana

Described by Böedecker in 1927, this comes from Tamaulipas in Mexico and is included in the series *Leucocephalae*. A truly globular plant, usually solitary at first, but later developing offsets. Tubercles are very closely set, with white wool and bristles in the axils, each areole bearing more than 30 white radial spines and 2–4 centrals that are tipped with brown. Flowers are about 1 cm ($\frac{3}{8}$ in) long, pale pink with a greenish throat and a deeper pink central line.

### M. geminispina

This may easily be confused with *M. klissingiana*. It is similarly globular in shape, and may be either solitary or clustering. It also has white woolly and bristly axils, with 20 white radial spines and 2–4 centrals to 4 cm (1$\frac{1}{2}$ in) or more long, whitish with blackish-brown tips. The flowers are rose-pink with a deeper reddish central line and about 1.5 cm ($\frac{5}{8}$ in) long. It was named by Haworth in 1824 and is found in Hidalgo, Veracruz and elsewhere in Mexico. Like *M. klissingiana* it requires a slightly calcareous compost.

### M. baumii

Named by Böedecker in 1926 and initially included in the genus *Dolichothele*, which is now a sub-genus of the same name within *Mammillaria*. This is found in low scrub in Tamaulipas, Mexico, near to San Vicente. It is a beautiful clustering species with pronounced areole-tipped tubercles and only slightly woolly axils. Appearing from the areoles are 36 or more white radial hair-like

*Mammillaria angelensis*

spines and 5–6 yellowish centrals almost 2 cm ($\frac{3}{4}$ in) long, a little longer than the radials. Flowers are about 3 cm ($1\frac{1}{4}$ in) long and wide, bright yellow and slightly scented. The fruits are greenish-grey and contain many brown seeds.

# MATUCANA

This has become one of several rather confused genera since the mid-1970s. It commenced in 1922 as a mono-typic genus of which the then *Echinocactus haynei*, so named by Otto in 1850, became the type species as *Matu-cana haynei*, when Britton and Rose established this genus. It is named after the village near Lima in central Peru where this particular species was discovered grow-ing among rocks. At first the genus appeared to be con-fined to globular or sometimes cylindrical species, and to a great degree the same applies today. Several species have been reclassified in *Borzicactus*, where apparently

they do not belong, as some have been returned to *Matu-cana*. It is now proposed that they should be merged with *Oreocereus* which, in the opinion of numerous cacto-philes, is equally unacceptable. At present the genera *Submatucana* and *Eomatucana* are synonyms of *Matu-cana*. Possibly *Arequipa*, a genus established by Britton and Rose in 1922, should also be involved, as it differs from *Matucana* only in the fact that the fruits, when they are fully ripened, burst open to disperse their seeds from the base.

In cultivation the species have proved exceedingly interesting and popular plants and respond well to care-ful attention. Many do not require really warm temper-atures; about 10°C (50F°) is likely to prove a satisfactory minimum level for all, and those, including the type species, that are endemic to high-altitude habitats are capable of accepting even less, although they sometimes prove more difficult to flower successfully. An ordinary cactus compost is suitable; water freely from April to October, but keep the plants dry during dormancy; an occasional feed in the growing season will encourage

flowering. All are sun-loving species and need the brightest possible position. They are readily propagated from seeds.

### M. haynei

This was described as *Cereus haynei* as early as 1878. The name honours Professor F.G. Hayne, a German botanist. The stems are globular or slightly elongated, possibly to about 30 cm (1 ft) tall and 8–10 cm (3–4 in) thick. There are 25–30 tuberculate ribs, with closely-set areoles bearing numerous brownish spines with blackish tips, a few of which are about 3.5 cm (1⅜ in) long. The flowers have long, slender tubes, about 7 cm (2¾ in) long, and carmine-red petals; they appear from the crown of the plant.

### M. aureiflora

Named by Ritter, this was previously included in *Submatucana* by Backeberg, and *Borzicactus* by John Donald. It is from Cajamarca in Peru and is dark greyish-green in colour, globular in shape, but somewhat flattened on the upper surface, with up to 27 tuberculate

*Mammillaria baumii*

ribs and areoles bearing many radial and a few central yellowish-brown spines; the centrals are longer than radials. Flowers are a bright golden-yellow, about 4 cm (1½ in) long and wide when fully open. It is one of the choicest of species and easy flowering.

### M. madisoniorum

First included by Paul Hutchison in *Borzicactus*, later by Backeberg in *Submatucana* and finally by Rowley in *Matucana*, this comes from the Amazonas region of Peru at altitudes of about 500 m (1650 ft). A quite large globular plant, rarely elongating, greyish-green or bluish-green in colour with a dull rough surface. There are 7–12 ribs, almost spineless; the spines that do form very soon fall away and at best are only about 3 cm (1¼ in) in length. Flowers are a rich vermilion, 8–10 cm (3–4 in) long.

### M. aurantiaca

Also from Cajamarca in northern Peru and first recorded by Vaupel as *Echinocactus aurantiacus*, it is a globular plant, occasionally forming offsets. It has about 10 ribs with elliptic-shaped areoles bearing 25 or more reddish-brown spines 1–5 cm ($\frac{3}{8}$–2 in) long. Flowers, 7–9 cm ($2\frac{1}{2}$–$3\frac{1}{2}$ in) long, are narrowly funnel-shaped, orange with reddish throats.

# MELOCACTUS

Plants of this genus constitute some of the earliest species brought into cultivation. Even before Linnaeus prescribed the name *Cactus* for all the species known in his day, the plants as we know them today were referred to as *Echinomelocactus*; this is from the Greek *echinos*, meaning prickly or spiny, and possibly a local name, *melones*, which probably refers to a fruit. They were only recognized under the generic name of *Cactus* until 1827 when Link and Otto established *Melocactus*, a shortened form of the original name. They are commonly known as the Turk's-cap cactus, from the principal feature of all the species, the cephalium. This begins to develop once a plant has reached maturity and the globular body ceases to grow; it is a central columnar growth, somewhat woody in the centre, densely covered with woolly hairs and sharp bristles. From this cephalium, which carries

*Matucana aureiflora*

numerous areoles, the flowers appear, never on the body of the plant. The genus is still undergoing considerable research, and at present includes about 60 species. They are native to some of the warmest areas of America, from southern parts of Mexico to northeasterly regions of Brazil, and to many of the West Indian islands.

All species can be readily grown from seeds, but it is important to remember that after germination, and indeed at all times, a temperature never less than 15°C (60°F) must be maintained. They take several years to reach maturity, and as they develop ensure there is ample space in the container to hold the spreading roots. After 5–8 years, when the cephalium begins to show, repotting will become almost unnecessary as the body will expand no further. From then on it is a matter of regular fertilizing so as to guarantee the growth of the cephalium and the appearance of the flowers. Use a very open compost; if using a proprietary cactus compost add one part of sharp gritty sand to two parts of compost. Always keep the plants in a sunny position; water carefully during the warmest months and give an occasional light spray with tepid water during winter. Propagation is by seeds sown in late winter and early spring.

### M. intortus

Named *Cactus intortus* by Philip Miller in 1768, this assumed its present name, at the instigation of Ignaz

*Matucana aurantiaca*

Urban, in 1919. It is native to the West Indian islands and can be quite variable from one island to another. In general, it is a globular plant with up to 20 deeply furrowed ribs and closely set areoles bearing many spines which are often 3 cm (1¼ in) long. The cephalium is one of the longest in the genus; with age it can reach well over 45 cm (1 ft 6 in) in length and is covered with brownish bristles and thick woolly hair. The flowers are pale pink, about 2 cm (¾ in) long, followed by reddish berry-like fruits, not unlike those of *Mammillaria*.

### M. matanzanus

From Cuba, the specific name identifying the habitat of Matanzas. Described by F.H. Leon in 1944, this is a much smaller plant, not exceeding 10 cm (4 in) across, with 8–9 well-arranged ribs and areoles bearing 7–8 radial spines, about 1.5 cm (⅝ in) long, and a single, slightly longer central. The cephalium is fairly shallow, yet pronounced, covered with reddish-orange bristles set in thick white wool. Flowers are pink, about 2 cm (¾ in) long.

### M. maxonii

Native to Guatemala, this was named *Cactus maxonii* by Rose in 1907, in honour of its discoverer, and the following year transferred to *Melocactus* by Gürke. It is a dark green globular plant about 10 cm (4 in) wide and 15 cm

(6 in) high, with about 14 round-edged ribs. The cephalium is only small and bears pinkish flowers about 4 cm (1½ in) long with whitish throats.

### M. violaceus

From Rio de Janeiro, this is one of several species from Brazil which have many similarities, and possibly they are just forms of one another. The specific name, prompted by Pfeiffer, refers to the reddish-purple spines, especially obvious in younger plants. A pale green plant, about 15 cm (6 in) broad at the base and only about 8 cm (3 in) high, it is topped with a low white cephalium set with brownish-violet spines and deep rose-pink flowers.

# MILA

A genus of fairly small plants, numbering about 12 and initially established for a single species by Britton and Rose in 1922. The generic name is an anagram of Lima, the capital city of Peru, near which the then only species was discovered. The plants have more or less cylindrical stems and branch freely to form clusters. They have low-set ribs with closely set spiny areoles. Flowers, on short scaly tubes, are produced at the

*Melocactus violaceus*

crown of the stems. In cultivation the plants need careful attention; a sunny, open position is ideal, and a fairly rich cactus compost must be free-draining. Water moderately during late spring and summer to the end of October; keep the plants dry during dormancy, at a minimum temperature of 13°C (55°F). Plants are still uncommon and sought-after by connoisseurs, but can be propagated with relative ease from seeds.

### M. caespitosa

The type species may attain 15 cm (6 in) in height; the stems are unlikely to be more than 3 cm ($1\frac{1}{4}$ in) thick. It is more or less of prostrate habit, but forming clusters. There are about 10 ribs set with brown areoles, each with about 20 yellowish radial spines, about 1 cm ($\frac{3}{8}$ in) long and generally tipped black, and 1–3 much longer centrals. Flowers, about 1.5 cm ($\frac{5}{8}$ in) long and 3 cm ($1\frac{1}{4}$ in) across, are deep yellow in colour with yellow style and stamens.

### M. nealeana

A species introduced by Backeberg, somewhat similar in size, habit and spination to the above. It forms offsets freely. The stem has about 11 flattish ribs with closely set yellow and woolly areoles, with about 12 white radials, no more than 1 cm ($\frac{3}{8}$ in) long, and 3–4 yellowish-brown, downward-pointing central spines about 1.5 cm ($\frac{5}{8}$ in) in length. The flowers, which are approximately 2.5 cm (1 in) wide with short tubes, are pale yellow.

# MONVILLEA

This is an interesting genus with slender, semi-erect stems, principally branching from the base and capable of forming thickets. It was established by Britton and Rose in 1920, honouring M. Manville, a French authority on cacti, and originally included only a few species, but further discoveries, together with the inclusion of *Praecereus* (and probably of *Brasilicereus*) in this genus will mean that many more species are involved. They are night-flowering plants, the blooms all appearing towards the top of the branches during the summer. They are native to Brazil, Argentina, Paraguay, Peru, Bolivia and Ecuador. All species are relatively easy in cultivation, several forming very attractive and sought-after plants, especially those that tend to develop cristate forms. An ordinary cactus compost and filtered light appear to suit them all. Water in moderation during the growing season but keep completely dry throughout dormancy, at a winter temperature of 10°C (50°F). Feed every 3–4 weeks during late spring and summer.

### M. cavendishii

From Brazil, Paraguay and Argentina, it was named in 1840 by Monville as *Cereus cavendishii* for the then Duke of Devonshire, W. Spencer Cavendish. Britton and Rose established its present status. It can reach more than 1 m (3 ft 3 in) in height. The stems are about 2.5 cm (1 in) thick, dark green in colour and with only a few branches. There are about 9 ribs set with quite small areoles bearing 8 radial spines and 1–4 centrals about 1.5 cm ($\frac{5}{8}$ in) long; they are slender, yellowish-white at first but turning brownish-black. Flowers, about 12 cm ($4\frac{3}{4}$ in) long, have tubes and open to about 10 cm (4 in) across; the outer flower segments are pinkish, the inner petals white.

### M. spegazzinii

Native of Paraguay, this is possibly the most decorative of the species – it frequently develops fascinating cristated growths. Originally placed in the genus *Cereus*, it was transferred by Britton and Rose to their new genus. The stems are dark bluish-green and beautifully marbled in greyish-white; they can grow to well over 3 m (10 ft) in length but rarely exceed 2 cm ($\frac{3}{4}$ in) in thickness, resulting in stems which are chiefly creeping or semi-climbing. Each stem has 4–5 almost angular ribs, with small areoles set well apart, 3–5 thick, black radials, about 4 mm ($\frac{1}{8}$ in) long, and very occasionally a single slightly longer central. Flowers, about 12 cm ($4\frac{3}{4}$ in) long, are pale pink externally, with creamy-white inner petals.

# MYRTILLOCACTUS

A small genus of 3–4 species whose number may well be doubled if, as is likely, other genera such as *Escontria* and *Heliabravoa* are included in the genus. It was established by the Italian botanist M. Console in 1897 to contain a single species, until then known as *Cereus geometrizans* and described by C.F. von Martius in 1837. The generic name refers to the fruits, which resemble those of the bilberry (*Vaccinium myrtillus*). All are tall, columnar, tree-like plants, with stems and branches 8–10 cm (3–4 in) in diameter and 5–9 ribs. The diurnal flowers are followed by small fruits, said to be edible. All species are native to Mexico, from Sinaloa southwards to Oaxaca, Guatemala and Baja California. In cultivation they are among the most popular of cacti. If provided with a bright sunny position, a rich cactus compost with a few limestone chippings added and careful watering, they will thrive and develop the rather unique colouring of their stems. Water regularly from April to October, then keep the plants dry until March – ideally at a minimum temperature of 10°C (50°F), although if kept very dry they will accept even lower temperatures. Feed at 4-weekly intervals during the growing season with a weak liquid fertilizer.

### M. geometrizans

A tree-like specimen, 3–4 m (10–13 ft) high, with a short, thick trunk and massed branches above, about 10 cm (4 in) thick, above. Its glory lies in the attractive colouring of the branches, generally bluish-green, but younger growth even more intensely blue. The 5–6 ribs are set with areoles 2 cm ($\frac{3}{4}$ in) or more apart; they bear 5–9 radial spines, about 1 cm ($\frac{3}{8}$ in) long, and one almost black central spine, 7 cm ($2\frac{3}{4}$ in) long. The flowers are greenish-white, about 3.5 cm ($1\frac{3}{8}$ in) wide when petals are fully spread, and with numerous white stamens and style. The fruits are purplish.

### M. cochal

First named *Cereus cochal* by C.R. Orcutt in 1889, this is another tree-like plant, growing to well over 1 m (3 ft 3 in) high and found only in Baja California. It has a fairly short trunk with several stumpy branches, each with 6–8 ribs and areoles carrying several blackish spines, sometimes 2 cm ($\frac{3}{4}$ in) long. Flowers, about 2.5 cm (1 in) long and wide when fully open, are pale greenish-white, with white style, stamens and stigma lobes. The fruits are deep red and said to be edible.

# NEOLLOYDIA

This genus was established by Britton and Rose in 1922. Their definition of the characteristics involved has led to questioning whether certain species at present in *Turbinocarpus*, *Normanbokea*, *Echinomastus*, *Pediocactus* and others really belong in these genera, because they all have certain features in common with those currently within *Neolloydia*. There is also a close relationship with *Thelocactus*, and it seems difficult to determine a final line of demarcation. The species mentioned here are considered correctly placed, and they include plants recently transferred from *Gymnocactus*. The generic name is a dedication to the American botanist, Professor Francis E. Lloyd. Plants are more or less cylindrical in shape, with tuberculate ribs arranged spirally, and most species possess extremely attractive spination. The tubercles have a groove or furrow above, and the colourful flowers develop at the base of the grooves of the younger areoles in the crown. All species require a very sunny, bright and warm position. A proprietary cactus compost provides a suitable growing medium, provided that it is free-draining. Water moderately throughout the growing and flowering season; a drying-out period between each application is most important. Keep completely dry during winter, at a minimum temperature of 10°C (50°F). Feed 3–4 times during the growing season when the weather is at its warmest. A few species produce offsets, which can be removed as cuttings; new plants are better raised from seeds sown in early spring.

*Myrtillocactus geometrizans*

### N. conoidea

First recorded by de Candolle as *Mammillaria conoidea*, this was adopted as the type species of *Neolloydia* when the genus was established. Native to Mexico, it is a most variable species, solitary or clustering, with about 8 ribs set with tubercles; the areoles have numerous spines almost covering the plant, and rich, highly coloured flowers enhanced by equally beautiful stamens, style and stigma lobes. The species earlier known as *N. grandiflora*, from Tamaulipas, is now var. *grandiflora* of *N. conoidea*. This has a cylindrical stem about 10 cm (4 in) high and 4 cm ($1\frac{1}{2}$ in) wide, with a few short tubercles set in the white woolly grooves. Areoles carry up to 25 white, spreading radial spines about 6 mm ($\frac{1}{4}$ in) long, and usually one black, 3 cm ($1\frac{1}{4}$ in) long, central spine. The flowers, almost 4 cm ($1\frac{1}{2}$ in) long, have widely spreading, deep violet-pink petals. *N. conoidea* var. *texensis*, known only from Texas and earlier recorded as *N. texensis*, is more globular in shape, about 6 cm ($2\frac{1}{2}$ in) high, the areoles bearing up to 15 radial spines about 1 cm ($\frac{3}{8}$ in) long and one or two longer centrals. Flowers are pinkish-violet, about 6 cm ($2\frac{1}{2}$ in) across when fully expanded. Another species, *N. ceratites*, has recently been reclassified to as *N. conoidea* var. *ceratites*. It has a stem about 10 cm (4 in) tall, often clustering, and greyish-green in colour; the 10 or more ribs, in pronounced spirals, have round woolly areoles bearing about 15 greyish-white radial spines, 1.5 cm ($\frac{5}{8}$ in) long, and 5–6 greyish, black-tipped centrals 3 cm ($1\frac{1}{4}$ in) long. Flowers are rich purple, about 3.5 cm ($1\frac{3}{8}$ in) long.

### N. subterranea

From Tamaulipas, Mexico, and described by Backeberg, this has been included in both *Gymnocactus* and *Rapicactus*. It owes its present classification to the American botanist H.E. Moore. It is a cylindrical-shaped plant about 10 cm (4 in) high and 3.5 cm ($1\frac{3}{8}$ in) thick. Areoles appear from each tubercle, bearing about 16 white, spreading radial spines, 6 mm ($\frac{1}{4}$ in) long, and two brownish-black centrals 1.5 cm ($\frac{5}{8}$ in) or more in length.

Flowers, nearly 4 cm (1½ in) across when fully open, are pinkish-purple with numerous yellowish stamens, a prominent style and stigma lobes.

### N. cubensis

A small, somewhat dwarf species from the Province of Oriente in Cuba. Before its transfer to this genus by Backeberg, it had been included by Britton and Rose in *Coryphantha*. This is a depressed-globose species with stems only about 3 cm (1¼ in) in diameter and numerous distinctly grooved tubercles with areoles bearing about 10 whitish-grey spines, 4 mm (⅛ in) long. The flowers are pale yellowish-green, 1.5 cm (⅝ in) long, with yellowish style, stamens and stigma lobes.

# NEOPORTERIA

When this genus was established by Britton and Rose in 1922, it included only 7 species; today the number would seem to be in the region of 80 or more. This is due to new discoveries, and to the merging of genera such as

*Neolloydia conoidea* var. *texensis*

*Neochilenia, Pyrrhocactus, Islaya, Reichocactus* and others under the one name. The generic name is partly from the Greek *neos*, meaning new, and partly in recognition of C.E. Porter, a Chilean entomologist. Most species are globular, a few becoming slightly elongated, and with but few exceptions they are greyish-green or brown in colour. The ribs are more or less tuberculate, many with large areoles and very spiny, in others the spines are scarcely discernible. The flowers, varying in colour, are generally borne from or near the crown of the plants. Many species are autumn-flowering, others bloom in spring. All are of South American origin, primarily Peru, Argentina and Chile. The plants are generally of easy culture, though those with tuberous rootstock require more care and particularly demand a compost more porous than those with fibrous roots. Use a fairly rich cactus compost for successful growing; careful watering is necessary as certain species of early or late-flowering are best given a short resting period in mid-summer.

Occasional feeding, say every 3–4 weeks, is beneficial, but only when plants are in growth. Maintain a winter temperature of 10°C (50°F). Propagation is by seeds sown in late winter and early spring.

### N. subgibbosa

The type species was described by Haworth in 1831 as *Echinocactus subgibbosus* and prior to the creation of this genus had been known under 12 or more different names, both generic and specific. Plants are variable, but either globular or slightly elongated; in cultivation, they may reach up to about 15 cm (6 in) in height and about 10 cm (4 in) in width. They are mainly greyish-green in colour, with some varieties a brighter green. There are 14–21 ribs with mainly well-defined areoles. In var. *subgibbosa* they carry 14–25 yellowish-grey radial spines and a few centrals, often almost black, and bright pinkish trumpet-shaped flowers about 4 cm (1½ in) long. The variety *litoralis*, which was once accorded specific status by Ritter, has a green stem, about 30 brownish or blackish, often yellowish and very fine radials and up to 12 central spines. Pinkish flowers are about 2.5 cm (1 in) long. Other forms include var. *castaneoides*, with a greyish-green body with areoles carrying up to 20 bright

*Neoporteria subgibbosa* var. *castaneoides*

yellow or yellow-brown radial spines and 4–6 centrals; flowers are reddish-pink with white inner petals. All are from Chile.

### N. nidus

From northern Chile, this also is most variable. It had been described by J. Söhrens as *Echinocactus nidus* in 1900. A globular species, 8–10 cm (3–4 in) high and wide, with 16–18 tubercled ribs and large areoles each with 30 or more whitish radial spines, some 3 cm (1¼ in) long; which densely cover the plant, and probably led to an earlier name, *E. senilis*, applied by Philippi in 1839. The 3–6 cm (1¼ in–2½ in) long flowers are pinkish-red.

### N. esmeraldana

From Esmeraldas in Chile, and placed in this genus by Donald and Rowley, this had previously been in *Neochilenia*. It is a small plant only 7 cm (2¾ in) wide and almost black in colour. The ribs are very tuberculate with white-tufted areoles, few or several radial and one central spine, all very fine and short. Flowers are densely spined around the base, about 5 cm (2 in) long, with yellowish-brown outer segments and silvery-white inner petals; they open to 4 cm (1½ in) or more across.

### N. napina

From Huasco in Chile, it was recorded as *Echinocactus napinus* by Philippi in 1872 and later labelled as *Notocactus napinus* by Berger. Backeberg brought it into *Neoporteria*. A plant about 10 cm (4 in) tall and 5 cm (2 in) thick, it is very dark greyish-green in colour. There are about 14 prominently tubercled ribs with white-felted areoles, each with about 10 very short blackish radial spines and 3–4 centrals, all spreading. The flowers, 2–3 cm (¾–1¼ in) long, are decidedly funnel-shaped and creamy-yellow with pale pink outer segments, long yellow stamens and a pinkish-red style.

# NEORAIMONDIA

A small genus of stout columnar plants from Peru, Bolivia and Chile, containing only two or perhaps three species. It was established by Britton and Rose in 1920 and acknowledged the work of Antonio Raimondi, the Peruvian geographer. It also includes the genus raised by Backeberg, *Neocardenasia*. The plants are tree-like in habit, sometimes forming quite dense clumps with branches growing from the base. There are only 4–8 ribs which carry very large areoles, more so near the tips of the branches where the diurnal flowers appear; they are generally spineless. The plants are of very slow growth and only rarely encountered in cultivation. They need a very bright position and high temperatures at all times; never below 18°C (65°F). Water sparingly, and only dur-

*Neoporteria nidus*

ing the main growing season when temperatures are at their highest. Keep completely dry in winter. Propagation is from seeds, but these are infrequently available.

### N. macrostibas

From western Peru, it was named *Pilocereus macrostibas* by Schumann in 1903, then two years later placed by Berger in *Cereus*, where it remained until it became the type species of the new genus. The species is tall-growing, about 4 m (13 ft) in habitat, and 10 cm (4 in) or more thick. The columnar habit is very pronounced, the branches developing stout and erect from the base of the plant. There are 5–8 ribs, with closely-set, large areoles, 1–6 cm ($\frac{3}{8}$–$2\frac{1}{2}$ in) long, the flower-bearing areoles being the largest. They are brown-felted, carrying about 12 radial spines, varying in length, and usually two centrals, 15 cm (6 in) or more in length. The areoles at the ends of the branches become compacted and mainly lack spines. Flowers are 4 cm ($1\frac{1}{2}$ in) long, scaly and bristly externally, the inner petals white and 1 cm ($\frac{3}{8}$ in) long. Style and stamens are white, stigma lobes pale pink.

# NEOWERDERMANNIA

A genus of about three species established in 1930 by the Czech cactus authority Alberto V. Frič, the name honouring the German botanist, Erich Werdermann. It is closely allied to *Gymnocalycium* and *Neoporteria*, varying only in minor details. These are Andean plants, found at altitudes of around 4000 m (13,000 ft) in Argentina, Chile, Bolivia and Peru. All are globular in shape with ribs defined by tubercles. Flowers are borne close to the crown from areoles centred between the tubercles and are followed by small fruits with only a few seeds. Particular care is required to grow the plants successfully: a bright sunny position is essential and the compost must be very permeable as the rootstock is in the form of a long taproot; any retention of moisture can quickly destroy it. Water regularly from April through to late September or early October, allowing the soil to dry out between waterings; feed with a weak liquid fertilizer every 4 weeks or so during the growing season. Keep totally dry throughout the whole period of dormancy from November to March, when minimum temperatures can fall to 7°C (45°F) without harm. Propagation is from seeds.

### N. vorwerkii

Named by Frič and for a while transferred to *Weingartia*, this has a greenish stem, globular in shape and about 8 cm (3 in) in diameter with 16 tuberculate ribs, the tubercles almost triangular in shape. The areoles are large, white-woolly, set in depressions between the tubercles, and bearing 7–10 slender and sharp radial spines, slightly curved and spreading, 1.5 cm ($\frac{5}{8}$ in) long, and one central of similar length, brownish-purple but becoming yellowish-grey. The flowers, about 2.5 cm (1 in) long and across, are funnel-shaped, white and pinkish-lilac in colour, opening from almost black flower buds.

# NOPALXOCHIA

This genus of easy and beautifully flowering cacti was established by Britton and Rose in 1923. The name is probably derived from the Aztek name *nopal*, referring to the flowers, which are similar to those seen on *Opuntia* species. It has a close affinity to *Epiphyllum*, and there are several inter-generic hybrids between species of these two genera. Some authorities consider the genus closer to *Disocactus* because of a number of similarities, but if it should be absorbed into either of these genera many would regret the passing of a popular genus. At present *Lobeira* and *Pseudonopalxochia* have been included within *Nopalxochia*. All species are epiphytic.

In cultivation they are excellent plants for the home or greenhouse, and if planted in hanging-baskets the flattened leaf-like stems can display their naturally pendent habit with numerous flowers adorning their length. A rich acid compost is essential, but it must be sufficiently porous to avoid unnecessary accumulation of excess water. Water freely throughout the year, but only enough to save the roots from drying out in winter. Feed every 3–4 weeks during the growing season. It is best kept in a position with filtered sun, at a minimum temperature in winter of 13°C (55°F). Propagation is by cuttings in summer.

### N. phyllanthoides

Native to the Puebla region of Mexico, this is the type species, initially recorded by de Candolle as *Cactus phyllanthoides* in 1813 and later included in *Epiphyllum*, in *Cereus* and even in *Opuntia*. The basal stems are slightly woody, but they produce elongated flattened, leaf-like branches 30 cm (1 ft) or more long and approxi-

*Nopalxochia phyllanthoides*

mately 5 cm (2 in) wide with slightly dentate margins. The flowers are pale to pinkish-red, 7 cm ($2\frac{3}{4}$ in) or a little more in length, with slender tubes, the petals either remaining closed or opening wide; they last for several days.

### N. ackermannii

This must be considered different, both in stem and flower structure, from the *Epiphyllum* of the same specific name. The *Epiphyllum* is definitely of hybrid origin, being the result of cross-pollination between *Nopalxochia phyllanthoides* and *Heliocereus speciosus*. In recent years, plants have been discovered growing wild in the Chiapas region of southern Mexico that are similar to *Nopalxochia* in stem growth – they do not have the thick, angled and sturdy growth apparent in the hybrids. The stems are flat, thin and leaf-like and of semi-pendent habit, the margins crenate, the day-flowering blooms are crimson, with pinkish style and stamens and white stigma lobes. These characteristics would seem to confirm the original description given by Haworth in 1829 for plants sent to him by G. Ackermann and named for him, thus proving the existence of the plant. Similar plants already flourish in Britain. They are far different

*Notocactus horstii*

in appearance from the lovely *Epiphyllum* cultivars which have graced the windowsills of numerous homes for more than a century. (See also *Epiphyllum*.)

Other species include *N. conzattianum*, previously designated *Pseudonopalxochia* by Backeberg, but now considered a variety of *N. ackermannii*. There is also a choice compact, red-flowering *N. horickhiia* more recently discovered species from Costa Rica.

# NOTOCACTUS

This genus is rapidly changing face and seems likely eventually to be absorbed into *Parodia*. Already those species that were earlier included in *Brasilicactus* and *Eriocactus* have been reclassified as *Parodia*, thus depriving *Notocactus* of many familiar species such as *N. leninghausii*, *N. graessneri*, *N. magnificus*, *N. claviceps* and *N. haselbergii*. The genus was established by K. Schumann in 1898, the name being from the Greek *noton*, referring to dry fruits. It currently includes the earlier recognized genera of *Malacocarpus* and *Wigginsia*. All are from South America, somewhat globular in shape, sometimes becoming partially elongated – they flower readily, having blooms near the crown. One very distinctive feature is apparent with most species, namely the prominent style, which is generally red or purplish, only rarely yellow. This protrudes conspicuously from the flower and the yellowish or pale orange stamens, and it certainly adds to the charm of the flower. In cultivation they need a bright location, though not necessarily in full sun. A rich porous compost should be provided, and regular watering throughout the growing and flowering period is essential. In winter they need to be kept fairly dry but, if a temperature of 13°C (55°F) is maintained, certain species may come into flower, in which case they should be given a little tepid water to prevent the soil from drying out completely. Propagation is from seeds, which should be sown early in the year at 21°C (70°F); young plants are likely to flower after the second year.

*Notocactus corynodes*

### N. ottonis

This popular species comes from Argentina, Uruguay, Paraguay and southern Brazil; it was placed in *Malaco-carpus* by Britton and Rose, then transferred to *Noto-cactus* by Berger. The body is globular, bright-green, to about 10 cm (4 in) across and with a woolly crown. There are 6–13 ribs, sometimes spirally arranged, bearing round areoles set about 1 cm ($\frac{3}{8}$ in) apart; each carries 8–15 or more yellow, spreading radial spines, straight or curved, and 3–4 reddish-brown centrals which are occasionally absent. Flowers are funnel-shaped, 4–6 cm ($1\frac{1}{2}$–$2\frac{1}{2}$ in) long and wide, rich glossy yellow, with yellow stamens and style and 14 deep red stigma lobes. A number of varieties are botanically recorded.

### N. horstii

This species originates from Rio Grande do Sul, Brazil, and was described by Ritter, the specific name honouring its discoverer. The plant body is solitary, about 13 cm (5 in) wide, with a spiny, woolly crown and 12–16 ribs. Areoles bear 10–15 pale brownish radial spines, 3 cm ($1\frac{1}{4}$ in) long, and 1–4 darker brown, slightly longer centrals. Flowers, 3–4 cm ($1\frac{1}{4}$–$1\frac{1}{2}$ in) long, are generally a rich vermilion with bright orange-yellow stigma lobes.

### N. corynodes

Native to Argentina, Uruguay and south Brazil, it was placed in both *Malacocarpus* and *Wigginsia*, before being given its present name by Hans Krainz. The plant body is globular or partially cylindrical, about 20 cm (8 in) high and 10 cm (4 in) wide, dark green with a densely woolly crown and 13–16 ribs, notched and distinctly thickened at the areoles. The 7–12 radial spines are deep yellow and 2 cm ($\frac{3}{4}$ in) long, sometimes with one longer central spine. Funnel-shaped flowers, up to 5 cm (2 in) long and wide, have bright canary-yellow inner petals and greenish yellow outer segments.

### N. purpureus

The rich colouring of the flowers justifies the specific title. A Brazilian plant, discovered and named by Ritter, it is 10–15 cm (4–6 in) wide, with about 15 ribs and numerous long radial and central spines with brownish tips. The large brilliant purple flowers cluster in the woolly crown and last for a number of days.

# NYCTOCEREUS

This small interesting genus was established in 1909 by Britton and Rose after intensive research by Alwin Berger. The generic name is from the Latin *nyct*, meaning night, and refers to the nocturnal flowering of the

*Notocactus purpureus*

species. Native to Central America, they are erect or clambering plants, with slender cylindrical stems and branches having many low-set ribs. Flowers are borne from the tips or sides of the branches, followed by reddish fruits with black seeds. The genus has a close affinity with *Peniocereus*, with which it may appropriately be merged; it currently includes about 6 species, some of which are extremely rare in cultivation. The plants are of relatively easy culture, accepting either a bright sunny position or one in partial shade; it is important that temperatures are never allowed to fall below 13°C (55°F). An ordinary cactus compost is suitable provided it is free-draining. Water freely from mid-April to October, but keep the plants completely dry during the dormant season. Add a weak liquid fertilizer to the water every 3–4 weeks during the growing period. Propagation is by seeds or cuttings.

### N. serpentinus

The type species chosen by Britton and Rose, has a long history going back to 1801 when it was described as *Cactus serpentinus* by the Spanish botanists M. Lagasca y Seguro and J.D. Rodriguez. It was said to come from Mexico, but its actual habitat has never been confirmed. It has long stems, often 5 m (16 ft 6 in) in length and 2–5 cm ($\frac{3}{4}$–2 in) thick, erect at first, then gradually becoming almost creeping and clambering. Ribs are low-set, 10–13 in number, with areoles at close intervals each bearing about 12 brownish-tipped white spines about 3 cm ($1\frac{1}{4}$ in) long. The flowers, borne towards the tips of the stems, are more or less funnel-shaped with bristly tubes; they have narrow white inner segments and pinkish-green outer segments. They are 15–20 cm (6–8 in) long and 8–10 cm (3–4 in) across when fully open. Fruits are bright red and densely spiny, about 5 cm (2 in) long and with large black seeds.

### N. guatemalensis

From El Rancho, Guatemala, the species was transferred to this genus in 1913 by Britton and Rose, having been first recorded by Vaupel, as *Cereus guatemalensis*. Stems are semi-erect or creeping, more than 1 m (3 ft 3 in) long and 3–6 cm ($1\frac{1}{4}$–$2\frac{1}{2}$ in) broad, with about 10 low rounded ribs and areoles with clusters of about 10 soft yellowish radial spines and three or more centrals, 4 cm ($1\frac{1}{2}$ in) long. The scented flowers, 20 cm (8 in) long, are red on the outside, pure white inside.

# OBREGONIA

The genus was established in 1925 by A. V. Frič for a solitary species native to Tamaulipas in Mexico. The

*Nyctocereus serpentinus*

name recognizes President Alvaro Obregón of that country. There is some question whether the genus should be included with *Strombocactus* because of the similarity of the flowers, but the species is so interesting and unusual that it should rightly be treated as exceptional and remain in *Obregonia*. The flat, leaf-like tubercles are an outstanding feature, to be compared only with some species of *Ariocarpus* with which there is doubtless an affinity.

### O. denegrii

A low-growing, globular plant 8–12 cm (3–5½ in) in diameter, somewhat flattened at the top and arising from a thick, fleshy taproot. Occasionally it develops offsets to form interesting clumps. The tubercles are greyish-green, 2–2.5 cm (¾–1 in) wide at the base, 1–1.5 cm (⅜–⅝ in) long, flat on the upper surface, but with a prominent keel on the undersurface. The areoles are set at the tips of the tubercles; when young they have a few bristly spines which fall off as the plants mature. Flowers occur in the centre of the plant; they are pinkish-white, 3–4 cm (1¼–1½ in) across, with many petals arranged in a funnel shape. Fruits are in the form of white berries. To grow successfully, keep the plant in full sun and provide a very porous, gritty soil. Water carefully during the growing season, but if the compost dries out too quickly during this period or if the general appearance looks brownish, move the plant to a position where it still enjoys good light, but is out of direct sun. Keep the plant completely dry during the winter dormancy period, at a temperature of 10°C (50°F). Propagation is by seeds during late winter or early spring.

## OPUNTIA

This is, without doubt, the best known of all Cactaceae. It has a long history, going back to 1754 when Philip Miller, the English botanist and gardener, established the genus, using the hitherto unpublished name given to these plants by French botanist Joseph de Tournefort. The name is said to be derived from *Opuntiani*, a tribe of ancient Greece, whose main city of Opus was near to Phocis, where the species *Opuntia vulgaris* is thought to have been first cultivated. Throughout the years, species have been added while others have been transferred elsewhere, and the process is continuing. Linnaeus referred to a *Cactus opuntia* in 1753, but the exact species is undecided; while it conceivably was *O. vulgaris*, the doubt persists, and the so-called type species remains unidentified. Miller brought together a number of now obsolete generic names such as *Cactodendron*, *Ficindica* and *Cactus* (of Lemaire) when he officially established the genus.

*Obregonia denegri*

Subsequently, it has undergone reclassifications when it was sub-divided into *Corynopuntia*, *Cylindropuntia*, *Marenopuntia*, *Platyopuntia* (an invalid name) and several others. These, together with genera which have proved acceptable for many years, such as *Tephrocactus*, *Nopalea*, *Consolea* and others, have now been incorporated under the single genus of *Opuntia*. The earlier grouping of some 130 species which was made in 1897 has now been expanded to close on 500 recognized specific names.

This widespread genus extends from southern parts of Canada to southern regions of Chile, with many species proving extremely variable. They had and have many common names ascribed to them, including 'prickly pear', 'cholla', 'tuna', etc., the names often referring to the stem structure.

Opuntias are one of the easiest cacti groups to grow successfully, but there are exceptions. The majority enjoy a bright sunny position – the more exposed to full light, the better. They seem readily to survive long periods of drought, but for best results water freely during the spring and summer months. Throughout the winter, however, restrict watering to the minimum, even keeping plants completely dry. Feeding during the growing and flowering season is advisable, about every four weeks from April to late September. A number require a minimum winter temperature of 10°C (50°F), while the

majority will accept extremely low temperatures, to below freezing as long as the soil is completely dry. Several can be regarded as hardy outdoor plants, but only if they are placed in a location where no excess moisture can accumulate and be retained around the rootstock. A good cactus compost will meet the needs of all species, whether they are grown as mature specimens or propagated from young stem cuttings. A similar compost is also suitable for seed sowing; it should be kept just moist, shaded from full sun and maintained where a minimum temperature of 21°C (70°F) can be guaranteed throughout the period of germination and for several weeks thereafter.

Few comprehensive collections of *Opuntia* species exist, but possibly the finest is to be seen at Pinya de Rosa, near Blanes in southeast Spain, where scarcely any known species is absent.

### O. vulgaris

Described by Miller in 1768, when he incorporated many names given to the same species by others, this is a tall-growing, tree-like plant capable of attaining 5 m (16 ft 6 in) or more in congenial conditions. Its exact habitat remains a mystery, possibly from northern parts of America. It is, however, naturalized in many parts of the world, even to becoming a nuisance plant in countries such as Australia. As a mature plant it develops a cylindrical trunk, about 13 cm (5 in) in diameter; the more or less oblong joints are bright green, 20 cm (8 in) or more long, and very thick and fleshy. Areoles are widely distributed on both upper and lower surfaces; they are quite woolly and bear one to three spines and – a characteristic found only in *Opuntia* – many brownish glochids or fine bristles, which easily become detached by contact. The flowers are reddish or yellow, the latter being the prime colour, and about 9 cm (3½ in) long and 5 cm (2 in) across. Fruits are about 7 cm (2¾ in) long and purplish-red. Plants have been cultivated in some parts of the world as host plants for the insects that yield the scarlet dye, cochineal.

### O. ficus-indica

One of the species named by Linnaeus in 1753, which he called *Cactus ficus-indica*. Miller provided the existing

*Opuntia microdasys*

name in 1768. The true wild habitat is uncertain, but it is widely distributed throughout warmer climates of the world, principally for the production of its fruit, the prickly pear. It is a tree-like plant which can measure up to 5 m (16 ft 6 in) tall, with more or less oblong joints 50 cm (30 in) or even more long. The areoles are small, producing numerous yellow glochids, sometimes a few or several spines, but very often spineless. Flowers are bright yellow, 10 cm (4 in) across when fully open and nearly 7 cm (2¾ in) long. The fruits, which are edible, are approximately 9 cm (3½ in) long; they are dull green, becoming pink then red.

### O. microdasys

Possibly the best known of the genus, this is frequently seen as a house plant. It is a North American plant, primarily from Mexico, although it has been said to originate from Brazil. The specific name was initiated by Charles A. Lehmann as *Cactus microdasys* in 1827; it was reclassified as *Opuntia* by Pfieffer years later. It is a variable species, especially in the colouring of the

glochids: those of var. *albispina* are white; those of, var. *rufida*, reddish-brown; those of the typical plant, usually called var. *pallida*, yellow. In the wild, plants can reach more than 60 cm (2 ft) in height, with soft and velvety joints, 10–15 cm (4–6 in) long, more or less oblong in shape, and without spines. The areoles are evenly distributed and conspicuous with their clusters of glochids. The flowers, which are approximately 5 cm (2 in) long and wide, are a pale yellow colour, and are often tinged with pinkish-red.

### O. humifusa

This is reputed to be the *Cactus opuntia* of Linnaeus, but it remains unproven. It was christened *Opuntia opuntia* by G.K. Karsten and given its current name in 1830 by Rafinesque-Schmaltz. *O. rafinesquei* is synonymous. It is one of the hardiest of cacti, coming from southerly parts of Canada to the more northerly United States. It is a low-growing, spreading plant with small, somewhat oval joints 8–15 cm (3–6 in) long, and dark-green in colour. Areoles are well separated and bear yellowish-brown glochids but only 1–3 yellowish, darker-tipped spines and these are usually absent. The flowers are a rich sulphur-yellow, deepening to reddish in the throat, and 9 cm ($3\frac{1}{2}$ in) long and wide.

### O. salmiana

Native to Brazil, Paraguay and northern Argentina where it abounds on low rocky hillsides, the species was named by Chevalier de Parmentier in 1837. It represents a different stem growth, being a bushy plant that produces many branches from the base. The branches are slender, 1–1.5 cm ($\frac{3}{8}$–$\frac{5}{8}$ in) thick, dark green to almost purplish and without tubercles. Areoles are small and woolly, with yellow glochids and few, if any spines, never more than 1.5 cm ($\frac{5}{8}$ in) long. The flowers are approximately 3.5 cm ($1\frac{5}{8}$ in) long and wide; and the buds develop red, but open to white, pale yellow or slightly pink. The deep scarlet fruits are small and berry-like. This species needs a minimum winter temperature of 10°C (50°F).

### O. pachypus

Described in 1904 by Schumann, who gave its habitat as the coastal regions of central Peru. It is a particularly interesting species and very uncommon in cultivation. It has erect cylindrical stems, often up to 1 m (3 ft 3 in) high and 5 cm (2 in) thick, which generally branch to create a candelabra-like appearance. All the branches are broadly tuberculate and bear leaves which soon fall; the woolly areoles are borne on the upper part of the tubercles and have yellow glochids and up to 30 downward-pointing spines about 2 cm ($\frac{3}{4}$ in) long. Flowers are bright scarlet and 6–7 cm ($2\frac{1}{2}$–$2\frac{3}{4}$ in) long.

Recommended winter temperature is 13–15°C (55–60°F).

### O. tunicata

Named in 1837 by Link and Otto, it was first referred to under the generic name of *Cactus* by Lehmann 10 years earlier; it has also been called (by J.C. Wendland) *O. furiosa*, probably a very suitable name considering the spiny formations along the stems. It comes from central Mexico and is also known in Ecuador and northern Chile. A spreading, bushy plant, usually growing to about 50 cm (20 in) tall, with branches developing in whorls and covered almost completely with white-sheathed spines about 5 cm (2 in) long. These emerge from the large white areoles, with their pale yellowish-brown glochids 5–10 in number, straight, stiff and barbed, redish in colour under the papery white sheath. Flowers, about 3 cm ($1\frac{1}{4}$ in) long and 5 cm (2 in) wide when fully open, are yellow or yellowish-green.

### O. verschaffeltii

A low-growing, densely clustering species from Bolivia. It was named by Cels, a French cactus enthusiast, in 1898. Stems rarely exceed 15 cm (6 in) in length and are

*Opuntia salmiana*

*Opuntia tunicata*

# OREOCEREUS

only about 1.5 cm ($\frac{5}{8}$ in) thick, each joint slightly globular but becoming cylindrical, dull green in colour and rather tuberculate. The joints also produce leaves which remain for quite a long while before falling. Areoles are rounded, with many white glochids and a few, possibly up to 5, hair-like, whitish spines that are approximately 6 cm ($2\frac{1}{2}$ in) in length. The flowers, which are long-lasting, are bright red in colour, very rarely orange, and they are approximately 4 cm ($1\frac{1}{2}$ in) long and wide.

Many other remarkable and attractive species exist, though frequently they are considered items only for the specialist collector. Two that never cease to intrigue enthusiasts are *O. clavarioides*, which is remarkable for its peculiar stem growth, and *O. vestita*, so named by Salm-Dyck in 1845, which has striking clusters of small brown spines against a background of white wool and hairs.

This small genus of columnar cacti has been popular for many years. It was established in 1909 by the Italian botanist V. Riccobono, the name indicating its habitat – the Greek word *oros* means mountain. They are very hairy and spiny plants, enjoying a position in full sun and, being mountain plants, accepting the often extreme temperature variation which occurs between day and night. They are closely related to *Cleistocactus*, particularly in flower structure, and, perhaps for the same reason, to some of the more globular species of *Matucana* and *Oroya*. The genus *Morawetzia*, erected by Backeberg, has been merged with *Oreocereus*. These most fascinating columnar cacti justify a place in every collection; their beauty is apparent whether the plants are tall or short, young or old; the white hairy, woolly crowns have won them the common name of 'Old man of the Andes'. They are tall-growing plants, often branching from the base to form quite thick bushy clumps. Flowers appear towards the terminal ends of the stems, or in some in-

Above left: *Oreocereus celsianus*; above: *Oreocereus doelzianus*

stances from the pseudocephalium, which develops in maturity on certain species. In cultivation they need to be placed in the brightest position possible and where there is no likelihood of high humidity prevailing. An ordinary cactus compost can be used with success, but it is essential that the mixture be especially free-draining, best achieved by the addition of gritty sand. Limestone chippings should be added to ensure alkalinity. Water freely throughout the growing and flowering periods, and keep the plants dry during winter, at a temperature of 7°C (45°F). Propagation is fairly easy, if slow, from seed.

### O. celsianus

Native to northerly parts of Argentina and southern Bolivia, this is the principal species, and the most variable within the genus. It had previously been included by Lemaire in *Pilocereus* and at one time also in *Cleistocactus*. A truly beautiful species with branches from the base, each attaining over 1 m (3 ft 3 in) in height and up to 12 cm (4½ in) thick. The stems have many rounded ribs, from 9 to more than 20 in number, bearing large white woolly areoles, set about 1 cm (⅜ in) apart, and having 7–9 yellowish-brown radial spines, 2 cm (¾ in) long, and one or more longer central spines together with numerous whitish hairs, which are especially apparent

near the top of the stems where they are long and massed, though not forming a cephalium. The flowers, 9 cm (3½ in) long, are reddish-brown on the outside, with pinkish-red inner petals; the floral tube is densely hairy.

### O. trollii

From the Bolivian Andes and recorded by Backeberg, this shorter-growing plant is rarely more than 60 cm (2 ft) high, with stems only about 9 cm (3½ in) thick. This, too, is a densely woolly species, massed with numerous white hairs, yellowish or reddish spines and flowers, about 4 cm (1½ in) long, in shades of red.

### O. doelzianus

The one-time *Morawetzia*, originally described by Backeberg, is a Peruvian species. A tall-growing plant with stems 1 m (3 ft 3 in) or more high, it has a tendency to branch freely from the base. There are about 10 ribs with areoles carrying about 15 radial and 4 central yellowish-brown spines. A pseudocephalium forms at the top of the stems and is densely set with bristles and wool. The flowers, about 10 cm (4 in) long, are rich carmine-red, sometimes with a bluish suffusion.

# PACHYCEREUS

This is a genus of very large, almost tree-like cacti native to Mexico. The generic name comes from the Greek *pachys*, meaning thick, which aptly describes the robust stems and branches of each species. The genus has seen many changes since the name was proposed by Berger and subsequently published, by Britton and Rose, in 1909. Some species have been removed from it, others, following reclassification, added, such as certain species from *Lemaireocereus*, a well-known name now obsolete. There is a close affinity with other Mexican genera, such as *Lophocereus*, *Pterocereus* and *Marginatocereus* (currently included in *Stenocereus*) and *Backebergia*.

The few species now contained in *Pachycereus* are among the giants of the Mexican landscape. They, with *Carnegia gigantea*, are typical of the images conjured up in the minds of people when cacti are discussed. They are columnar in growth, developing bushy or tree-like proportions, but in cultivation the more majestic features are unlikely to emerge. They require a well-lit and sunny position and a very porous, preferably calcareous, soil, although an ordinary cactus compost is suitable, especially if some limestone chippings are added. Water can be given in moderation throughout the growing season, but a completely dry dormancy at a minimum temperature of 10°C (50°F) is essential from November through to late March. Give a diluted liquid fertilizer two or three times in summer, never more. Seed sowing, early in the year, is possibly the only method of propagation away from the natural habitat. The seeds are large and should be firmly set in the seed compost and covered with gritty sand to about their own depth. Keep at a temperature of around 21°C (70°F), provide a shaded position until germination has taken place, then give more light as the seedlings develop, but maintain the same temperature.

## P. pringlei

From Sonora in northern Mexico and Baja California, this is one of the largest cacti known; in some areas they capture the countryside with their magnificence. When first named it was referred by S. Watson to the genus *Cereus*, but it has also been known under different names and in other genera, such as *Pilocereus*. Plants can reach well over 10 m (33 ft) in height, with a diameter of about 1 m (3 ft 3 in), commencing to branch from about 1.5 m (5 ft) above ground level. Trunk and branches have 10–16 prominent ribs closely set with large grey-woolly areoles and about 20 or more reddish-brown, 3 cm ($\frac{1}{4}$ in) long radial spines which ultimately turn greyish, and one to three longer centrals. The bell-shaped flowers, about 7 cm ($2\frac{3}{4}$ in) long, are white on the inside, reddish-green on the outer surface; they appear towards the upper part of the stem and branches and are day-flowering.

## P. pecten-aboriginum

This has much the same habitat as *P. pringlei* but is perhaps more common in Chihuahua. It is a tall plant and in its natural habitat grows to about 8 m (26 ft) high, becoming tree-like in appearance with many erect branches from about 1.5 m (5 ft) above ground. Ribs are very pronounced with close-set areoles each with 8–10 thick, rigid, 3 cm ($\frac{1}{4}$ in) long radial spines of greyish-brown, and one or two centrals. It is said that the native Indians use sections of these spiny ribs as combs, hence possibly the specific name. The flowers are quite succulent and about 7 cm ($2\frac{3}{4}$ in) long, with white inner petals, purplish-red on the outside.

## P. weberi

From southerly parts of Mexico around Oaxaca, this is perhaps better known as *Lemaireocereus weberi*, a name given it by Britton and Rose in 1909 before it was transferred by Backeberg to *Pachycereus*, which is undoubtedly its rightful place. This, too, is a tree-like species, growing about 10 m (33 ft) tall, sometimes offshooting from the base, but more often branching from well above ground level. The stems are bluish-green, with about 10 prominent ribs set with large, rather elongated white

*Pachycereus pringlei*

woolly areoles at close intervals. Each areole has about 12 radial spines, yellowish-brown becoming reddish, 3 cm (1¼ in) long, and one or two almost black centrals, 10 cm (4 in) in length. The flowers are creamy-white and about 10 cm (4 in) long.

# PARODIA

A large genus of attractive and sought-after plants, all of which are native to South America. It was established by Spegazzini in 1923, the generic name acknowledging the work of the Argentinian botanist, L.R. Parodi. It is generally assumed that the many species currently embraced are rather small, globular or partially elongated plants with many ribs, straight or spirally arranged, with numerous tubercles or warts. The outstanding feature is the cluster of brilliantly coloured flowers borne near the crown of the plants. It is probable that several species currently contained within other genera belong to *Parodia*; a number of plants earlier included in *Notocactus* have already been reclassified, and taxonomists are considering further transfers which may eventually result in the disappearance of other well-known generic names.

When the species first found their way into collections in Europe, they were thought to be difficult to cultivate and were therefore grafted on to stocks of *Trichocereus*.

Far from being difficult, *Parodia* species offer only little challenge to successful growing. Good light is of paramount importance; without this, the plants are likely to lose the brilliance of their colourful spines. A fairly rich, open cactus compost is suited to their culture, and careful watering at all times. Maintain a winter temperature of about 10°C (50°F); in summer avoid exposure to too much heat, and if this is unavoidable ensure good ventilation. Propagation is easy from seeds, best sown in February or March; they are very fine and should be lightly sprinkled over the surface of the seed compost and carefully watered in. Keep them shaded, at a temperature of about 21°C (70°F); germination may be slow, but rewarding.

### P. chrysacanthion

This species became popular when it was first described as *Echinocactus chrysacanthion* by Schumann in 1898, but it remained difficult to obtain until well into the 1930s. Backeberg moved it into *Parodia*. In the wild it is found only in the provinces of Salta and Jujuy in Argentina. An attractive globular plant, more than 10 cm (4 in) high and wide, the spiralled ribs divided up into tubercles and the whole plant densely covered with numerous golden-yellow spines, very fine and straight

*Parodia saint-pieana*

and about 2 cm ($\frac{3}{4}$ in) long. The crown is thickly set with yellowish wool from which bright yellow flowers, each about 2 cm ($\frac{3}{4}$ in) long and wide appear.

### P. saint-pieana

Named by Backeberg soon after its discovery in Jujuy in Argentina, it is a clustering species, each separate body about 5 cm (2 in) high and broad. Ribs are clearly defined with many tubercles, the areoles carrying about 16 very short and straight, yellowish-brown spines. The flowers are bright yellow, about 2.5 cm (1 in) across.

### P. graessneri

From Rio Grande do Sul, Brazil, this species was transferred by F. Brandt in 1982 from *Notocactus*. It was first described as *Echinocactus graessneri* by Schumann in 1903, subsequently placed in *Malacocarpus* by Britton and Rose, then moved into *Brasilicactus* by Backeberg before being included by Berger with *Notocactus*. It is a rather flattened and rounded species, about 6 cm ($2\frac{1}{2}$ in) high and 10 cm (4 in) or more wide, covered with more than 50 tubercled ribs more or less spirally arranged. Numerous bright yellow spines, radials and centrals, about 2 cm ($\frac{3}{4}$ in) long, are carried on the closely set

*Parodia graessneri*

areoles. The flowers are small, greenish-yellow in colour and appear near the spiny crown.

### P. magnifica

Another of Brandt's transfers from *Notocactus*, this was earlier recorded as *Eriocactus magnificus*. This, too is from Rio Grande do Sul; it is globular, becoming elongated, frequently offsetting freely so as to form large clusters. The body of the plant is bluish-green, 10–15 cm (4–6 in) thick, with up to 15 symmetrically arranged ribs; the areoles are mainly felted, with numerous whitish radial spines and 10 or more slightly longer centrals. Flowers are centred around the crown; they are bright sulphur-yellow and about 5 cm (2 in) across.

### P. leninghausii

This also has been moved by Brandt into this genus from *Notocactus*, is from the same region of Brazil, and was initially included by F.A. Haage, Jr., in *Pilocereus* in 1895 when the plant was considered something of a mystery; in due course it was listed in *Malacocarpus*, then *Eriocactus* before being reclassified under *Notocactus* by Berger. This is one of the most popular of cacti with its bright golden-spined stem and angled, sloping crown. It starts as a somewhat globular plant but with age becomes almost columnar, nearly 1 m (3 ft 3 in) high and about 10 cm (4 in) thick. It has about 30 ribs with densely set

Above left: *Parodia magnifica*; above: *Parodia maassii*

areoles bearing up to 15 hair-like, yellow radial spines and 3–4 bristly, brighter yellow centrals, all about 4 cm (1½ in) long. The flowers are the transcending feature, pure clear yellow and opening wide to about 5 cm (2 in) across, especially striking with the bright yellow style and clustering stamens.

### P. maassii

A most variable species from Bolivia and Argentina where it grows in rocky terrain on high mountain slopes. When introduced in 1907 by the German collector E. Heese, it was named as a species of *Echinocactus*; it was eventually reclassified as *Malacocarpus* before being given its present status by Berger. It is about 20 cm (8 in) high and around 15 cm (6 in) in diameter, often dark yellowish-green, with somewhat spiralled ribs sometimes scarcely discernible near the base. The aeroles have up to 15 whitish radial spines, about 1 cm (⅜ in) long, and up to 4 hooked central spines about 4 cm (1½ in) in length. Flowers are reddish-purple, around 4 cm (1½ in) long and 1.5 cm (⅝ in) across. The variable forms include var. *subterranea*, from Cinti in Bolivia, and originally described as a separate species; it is a smaller plant with a white woolly crown, white and almost black spines and deep red, near purple flowers about 3 cm (1¼ in) long. Var. *rubida* has whitish radial spines and 3–6 curved centrals,

black-brown in colour and borne from woolly areoles; the flowers are rich carmine-red.

### P. mutabilis

Native to the region of Salta in Argentina, this is one of the better known species of the genus. It was named by Backeberg. It is a more or less globular plant, about 8 cm (3 in) in diameter, with spiralled, closely set ribs divided into tubercles. The areoles are white and woolly, each carrying about 50 hair-like, white radial spines, 1 cm (⅜ in) long, and 4 slightly longer, red or orange hooked centrals. The flowers, about 4 cm (1½ in) across, are usually clear yellow, sometimes they are enhanced with a red throat.

### P. gracilis

Native to Mendez in Bolivia, where it was discovered and named by Ritter, this is similar to, and possibly merely a form of, *P. procera*. It is a spherical plant, about 10 cm (4 in) in diameter, often much less. It has 13–16 or more ribs, which tend to become tuberculate with age. The areoles bear 14–22 radial and 4–10 central spines, all brownish, the central spines frequently hooked at the tips, especially on younger plants.

# PEDIOCACTUS

This includes a group of plants which has intrigued cactus enthusiasts over many years. It was established by Britton and Rose in 1913, the name coming from the Greek *pedi*, meaning plain, a reference to the plants' natural habitat on high open plains. It is one of the most difficult genera to define adequately; it has affinities with *Neolloydia, Sclerocactus, Turbinocarpus* and others, but a precise line of demarcation between many genera is difficult to determine satisfactorily. The genera *Pilocanthus, Utahia* and *Navajoa* are currently considered synonymous, and species contained therein have been reclassified in *Pediocactus*. All are from the southwestern parts of the USA, in habitats which vary considerably from low to high altitudes. They are mainly globular or short cylindrical plants, often with many ribs, sometimes tuberculate. The flowers appear in, or very near to, the crown.

*Parodia gracilis*

The plants are considered among the rarest of all cacti; some are thought to be almost extinct in the wild. Cultivation is by no means simple – the species often do best if grafted on to more robust stock, such as *Trichocereus*. Being principally mountain plants, they are accustomed to a pronounced difference between day and night temperatures and such contrasts are difficult to provide in cultivation. A cool winter resting period is essential, at a minimum temperature of 10°C (50°F). Very careful watering is demanded at *all* times; the plants will accept long periods of being dry, and as the actual growing season is uncertain, close observation is essential. As growth, or flowering, becomes apparent, be it in summer or winter, watering becomes of paramount importance; weak liquid feeds should be applied only when growth is obvious. Keep the plants in a well-lit position.

## *P. simpsonii*

Referred to *Echinocactus* in 1863, and subsequently adopted by Britton and Rose as the type species of *Pediocactus*, this is found at altitudes of 2000 m (6500 ft)

*Pediocactus simpsonii*

or more in many parts of USA (Arizona, New Mexico, Nevada, Washington, etc). In many ways it resembles *Mammillaria*, possessing distinct tuberculate ribs. The plants can attain 20 cm (8 in) or more in height and 15 cm (6 in) wide. The areoles are set on the tubercles and bear 25 or more yellowish-white radial spines, 1 cm ($\frac{3}{8}$ in) or more long, and 1–7 brown centrals, 2.5 cm (1 in) long. The flowers are bell-shaped, generally pink or white, rarely yellow; they are about 2.5 cm (1 in) long, with sulphur-yellow stamens and greenish-yellow style and stigma lobes.

Some species, now definitely included in *Pediocactus*, are of special interest; they have until recently been classified in other genera and include *P. sileri*, which was earlier *Utahia sileri*. This is a fascinating little plant. It is found in Utah/Arizona border country and is 10–15 cm (4–6 in) tall and up to 12 cm (4$\frac{1}{2}$ in) wide, having 13–16 ribs with closely set tubercles. Areoles each carry 11–15 whitish radial spines up to 2 cm ($\frac{3}{4}$ in) long and 3–7 slightly longer, black centrals, usually curved upwards. The yellowish flowers are approximately 2.5 cm (1 in) in length.

### P. peeblesianus

Previously classified by Leon Croizat in the genus *Navajoa* and transferred to this genus by Lyman Benson,

this is another most colourful species, only 7 cm (2$\frac{3}{4}$ in) high and 2.5 cm (1 in) wide. The spination is of particular interest; each areole bears 3–7 radial spines and a single central, yellowish-brown, almost corky, 1–3 cm ($\frac{3}{8}$–1$\frac{1}{4}$ in) long and curved upwards. The flowers, which are approximately 1.5 cm ($\frac{5}{8}$ in) long, are yellowish or pinkish-white in colour.

# PELECYPHORA

A genus established by Ehrenberg in 1843 to contain a single species. The generic name is from the Greek *pelekys*, meaning hatchet, and *phoros*, meaning bearing, referring probably to the shape of the tubercles. The plants are small and globose, covered with compressed tubercles which are arranged spirally. These, together with the attractive formation of the spines, constitute the main characteristics. It seems likely that Berger's genus *Encephalocarpus* will be united with *Pelecyphora*, although in many ways it has a closer affinity with *Ariocarpus*. Plants are quite rare in cultivation; they are very slow-growing but by no means difficult. A bright position is important, good light but not necessarily in full sun. A richy gritty and permeable compost is essential. Careful watering is required throughout the growing season; the plants should be kept dry in winter. Maintain a minimum temperature of 10°C (50°F) at all times. Propagate from seeds.

### P. asseliformis

From San Luis Potosi and Nuevo León in Mexico, it is a small plant, 5–10 cm (2–4 in) high and 2–5 cm ($\frac{3}{4}$–2 in) thick, dull greyish-green in colour, with hatchet-like tubercles, which are laterally compressed and cover the body in spiralling rows. Areoles are borne on the tips of the tubercles, which are elliptic in shape, with numerous minute white spines set in a comb-like formation. (Ehrenberg described this feature as 'an elongated, scale-like spine with numerous lateral ridges, usually free at the tip, giving a peculiar pectinate appearance'.) The flowers are 3–4 cm, ($\frac{1}{4}$–1$\frac{1}{2}$ in) across, funnel-shaped, with pinkish-violet inner petals, the outer segments whitish, stamens and style are white, the stigma lobes yellowish-orange.

*Pelecyphora asseliformis*

# PENIOCEREUS

When this genus was established by Britton and Rose in 1909 it was for one species only, *P. greggii*; currently 10–11 species are included. It seems likely that the genera *Neoevansia* and *Cullmannia*, which are barely distinguishable in most characteristics, do in fact belong to *Peniocereus*, as does *Nyctocereus*. The generic name is from the Greek *penis*, meaning thread, and refers to the very slender and thin stems of this clambering, semi-erect group of cacti from the United States and Mexico. Another feature, seen in some species, is the very substantial, fleshy rootstock, often in the form of an elongated taproot. Flowers are nocturnal, with long funnel-shaped tubes, and are followed by oval-shaped fruits said to be edible. These remarkable desert plants are uncommon in cultivation, but are relatively easy to grow. A very porous compost is necessary, which should be enriched with decayed humus. A lightly shaded position is advisable as the plants naturally associate with low-growing scrub into which they twine their stems for sup-

port. Careful watering is required, even in summer when plants are growing and flowering; feed at four-weekly intervals from June to September. A winter temperature of 10°C (50°F) is ideal, while the plants enjoy a period of complete dormancy. It is important to provide good-sized containers so as to avoid the fleshy roots becoming compressed in the pots.

### P. greggii

Originally named by Engelmann in 1848 as *Cereus greggii*, this was later made the type species of the genus by Britton and Rose. It is found in the southern United States and northerly areas of Mexico. The rootstock can be enormous, in habitat up to 60 cm (2 ft) in diameter and weighing more than 50 kg (110 lb). Stems are many, up to 3 m (10 ft) long and 2.5 cm (1 in) thick, dark grey, almost black-green in colour. The 3–6 ribs form somewhat angular stems, the edges of which are closely set with small woolly areoles bearing 7–11 very small black radial spines, and sometimes one or more equally small centrals. The flowers are borne on the sides of the stems; they are about 20 cm (8 in) long; with scaly, hairy tubes, and are 8–10 cm (3–4 in) wide when fully open, pure white in colour and sweetly scented.

Other species include *P. johnstonii*, from Baja California, which is similar to the above, but with slightly smaller flowers of pale pinkish-white, and *P. diguetii* which was described by Weber as a *Cereus* in 1895 and later made the type species of the genus *Neoevansia* by Marshall, is found near the shores of the Gulf of California in Sonora and Sinaloa in Mexico. Characterized by a long thick taproot, it has long dark green, almost black-green, stems only 8 mm ($\frac{1}{3}$ in) thick with 6–9 ribs. The small white areoles each bear about 10 radial and two central minute whitish spines. Flowers, approximately 10 cm (4 in) long, open to a pinkish or white bloom and measure 6 cm ($2\frac{1}{2}$ in) across.

# PERESKIA

The origin of the name goes back to 1703, when Plumier used it for just one species. Then E.G. von Steudel bestowed the name *Peireskia* upon the genus, in honour of a Frenchman, C.F. de Peiresc. Philip Miller reverted to the original name in 1754. It appears also to be one of the 22 species of *Cactus* included by Linnaeus. The plants are widely distributed through parts of Central and South America, Mexico and some of the West Indian islands. It is thought that the species form a 'primitive' group of cacti on account of similarities with species of other plant families. The genus is closely allied to *Rhodocactus* and considered synonymous by some authorities. There are 10, probably more, species included in the genus.

Pereskias are climbing, spreading, bushy and often tree-like plants, only partially succulent, with the distinction of possessing true leaves. They are easy in cultivation and can be grown very successfully in an ordinary cactus compost, given a position where they receive good light though not necessarily full sun. Water regularly and freely throughout the growing and flowering season, and lightly on occasions during the winter months; they dislike too long periods of complete dryness. Maintain a minimum temperature of 10°C (50°F). Propagate by cuttings in summer.

### P. aculeata

The species is widely distributed in Mexico and the West Indies, parts of southern Brazil and Florida, USA. Following the Linnaeus classification of 1753, it became known under several names including *Pereskia pereskia*, eventually assuming the present name designated by Miller. It is a rampant climber in habitat, but can be restricted successfully in a reasonably sized container. The stem develops many branches spreading from 3–10 m (10–32 ft); they are slender with few or many scattered areoles, each bearing two or three sharp spines, about 3 cm ($1\frac{1}{4}$ in) long, short-stalked, oval-lanceolate leaves, about 7 cm ($2\frac{3}{4}$ in) long (which in cultivation are often deciduous), and flowers. The rose-like flowers are particularly attractive, sweetly scented and usually borne in panicles, white or creamy-white, sometimes pink in colour and approximately 4.5 cm ($1\frac{3}{4}$ in) across at the tips. The fruits are yellow and spiny. Rooted cuttings make excellent grafting stock for many other cactus species, particularly the epiphytes. The variety *godseffiana* differs from *P. aculeata* only in having reddish-purple leaves.

### P. bahiensis

From the state of Bahia in Brazil and described by Gürke, this is a tall-growing tree-like or shrubby plant, about 8 m (26 ft) high, with slender branches (which become rather woody with age), and leaves about 9 cm ($3\frac{1}{2}$ in) long. Strangely, the areoles do not appear to produce spines until growth is well advanced. Then spines, about 9 cm ($3\frac{1}{2}$ in) long, are borne in plenty, 40 or so to each areole. The flowers are about 4 cm ($1\frac{1}{2}$ in) long, pale pink and borne in panicles.

### P. pititache

Described by Wilhelm von Karwinsky in 1837, it was later called *P. conzatti* by Britton and Rose, but this is now considered synonymous. A tall, branching shrubby plant, about 10 m (33 ft) high, native to Mexico (Oaxaca, Tehuantepec) and possibly Guatemala, it has rounded leaves about 2–2.5 cm ($\frac{3}{4}$–1 in) long and wide, the areoles bearing spines about 3 cm ($1\frac{1}{4}$ in) long, whitish-pink or pink flowers, 3 cm ($1\frac{1}{4}$ in) long, and pear-shaped fruits 2–3 cm ($\frac{3}{4}$–$1\frac{1}{4}$ in) long.

# PERESKIOPSIS

This genus was established by Britton and Rose in 1907 to contain a few tree- or shrubby-like plants, similar in some respects to those of *Pereskia*. The name, sometimes spelt *Peireskiopsis*, literally means 'like a Pereskia'. *Pereskiopsis*, though, differs from *Pereskia* in that the species have not only spines but also glochids, and because of this they are more closely allied to *Opuntia* than to *Pereskia*. Like the latter, the plants have leaves which develop from the areoles, but the flowers are borne laterally, like those of most *Opuntia*. There are probably about 12 species, all of which are native to Mexico and Guatemala. In cultivation the plants require a reasonably bright position; full sun is not essential, but avoid any tendency to extreme shade. An ordinary cactus compost suits all species as long as it is free-draining. Water freely during the spring and summer months, but keep the plants barely moist from November until March at a minimum temperature of 10°C (50°F). Feed at 4-weekly intervals from May to September. Propagation is easy from cuttings taken immediately after flowering; allow the cuts to callus before inserting in a mixture of sand and peat. Alternatively, increase from seeds – though these are difficult to obtain.

### *P. porteri*

As *Opuntia brandegeei*, the name given it by Schumann, this became the type species of the genus. Found in Sinaloa in Mexico and in southern parts of Baja California it is a thick shrubby plant about 1 m (3 ft 3 in) high, the stems often elongating, and about 3 cm ($1\frac{1}{4}$ in) thick. Areoles bear few or many spines, those on older growth having considerably more spines, some 5 cm (2 in) in length; new growth is more often than not spineless for the first two or three years. The leaves are oval with a pointed tip, quite fleshy, and about 3 cm ($1\frac{1}{4}$ in) long. Flowers are bright yellow and about 4 cm ($1\frac{1}{2}$ in) across when fully open; they have no tubes. The 5 cm (2 in) long fruits are deep orange or orange-red.

### *P. pititache*

Once classed by Karwinsky as a *Pereskia*, it is from southerly parts of Mexico, and possibly the best-known of the genus. Tall-growing, to about 3 m (10 ft), it branches occasionally, the branches being mainly slender for a few years and inclined to spread horizontally. The areoles bear a few spines, about 3 cm ($1\frac{1}{4}$ in) long, small bunches of yellow glochids and leaves about 4 cm ($1\frac{1}{2}$ in) long, more or less oblong with a slightly pointed tip. The flowers are creamy-yellow.

### *P. velutina*

Described by Rose in 1907, *P. velutina* comes from central parts of Mexico, particularly around San Luis Potosi. Rather shrub-like, it often forms quite dense growth in habitat, attaining 2m (6 ft 6 in) in height. The stems are slender, about 1 cm ($\frac{3}{8}$ in) thick, and covered with minute soft hairs. Leaves are lance-shaped, about 6 cm ($2\frac{1}{2}$ in) long, pointed at both ends and with numerous tiny velvety hairs over both surfaces. The areoles have long whitish hairs, a few whitish spines and glochids. The flowers are yellow and greenish-red on the outside. One of the most pleasing of the genus and very useful as grafting stock.

# PFEIFFERA

This genus contains a small number of South American plants, principally from Bolivia and Argentina. They are forest or woodland plants, of either pendent or semi-erect growth. The genus was established by Salm-Reifferscheid-Dyck in 1845 to contain a single species which had previously been recorded as a miniature *Cereus*. The name acknowledges Dr Ludwig Pfeiffer, a German physician and botanist whose explorations and research proved invaluable to the understanding of Cactaceae. This solitary species became *Pfeiffera cereiformis*, superseding Monville's *Cereus ianthothele*. There is a close affinity between this genus and *Rhipsalis*, and this particular species was recorded within that genus in 1846, and again in 1902 when the specific name reverted to *ianthothele*; this name appears to relate to the stem peculiarities. The plants are of easy culture, requiring a position in filtered light, out of direct sun. Provide a rich acid compost, which should be very porous, and maintain a minimum temperature of 13°C (55°F) at all times. It is wise to keep the soil barely moist during the period of dormancy, but water freely in the growing season. The plants flourish in hanging-baskets.

The genus *Pfeiffera* is scheduled for a possible reclassification; it may be merged with *Lepismium*, together with species of *Acanthorhipsalis* and *Lymanbensonia*, all of which may be distinguished by their reddish or black fruits.

### *P. ianthothele*

The type species is an epiphyte from Tucumán in northern Argentina. Its hanging branches are generally 4-angled, frequently spiralled, about 30 cm (1 ft) or slightly more in length and about 1.5 cm ($\frac{5}{8}$ in) wide. The ribs are tuberculate, with areoles set about 1 cm ($\frac{3}{8}$ in) apart, each carrying 6–7 short bristly, yellowish spines. The flowers are creamy-white, pinkish on the outer petals, about 2.5 cm (1 in) long with petals spreading slightly at the tips; the ovary is purplish and has

Above left: *Pfeiffera ianthothele* var. *tarijensis*; above: *Pilosocereus palmeri*

numerous bristles. The spiny red fruits are berry-like. Two varieties have been recorded: var. *boliviana* and var. *tarijensis*, neither of which varies to any appreciable degree from the type plant, although both are native to Bolivia.

### P. gracilis
Of Bolivian origin and introduced by Ritter, this tends to be of creeping habit, with elongated 5- or 6-angled branches which extend to about 60 cm (2 ft). The stems are about 6 mm ($\frac{1}{4}$ in) wide, with pale brownish spines, 6 mm ($\frac{1}{4}$ in) long, appearing from each of the 5–10 areoles. The flowers are diurnal, cream-coloured and about 2 cm ($\frac{3}{4}$) long. Fruits are reddish.

### P. multigona
Also from Bolivia and originally described by Cardenas in 1964, this, like the species *P. mataralensis*, varies but little from the type species.

# PILOSOCEREUS

This genus contains a group of plants that have exercised the minds of botanists for many years. It was established by R.S. Byles and Gordon Rowley in 1957, perhaps replacing the genus *Pilocereus* initiated by Schumann, in which characteristics were not clearly defined. The name is from the Latin *pilosus*, meaning hairy, which well describes these species, all of which feature long hairs along their stems. The genera *Cipocereus* and *Pseudopilocereus* are synonymous. The genus includes possibly 50 or more species, native to the USA, the West Indies, Mexico, Central America and many parts of South America. All are columnar plants, some becoming tree-like, others branching from the base to form large bushy clumps. Flowers in most species are produced from the terminal ends of the stems, protruding through the woolly pseudocephalium which develops with maturity. Flowering is nocturnal. Most species were, at one time, associated with the genus *Cephalocereus*, and while there may seem to be many similarities, their inclusion in that genus seems unwarranted as they are cephalium-forming plants.

Cultivation of these species is by no means difficult or complicated. Provide a good sunny position, as bright as possible, notwithstanding that some species are associated with light wooded country in the wild, and there experience a degree of shade. An ordinary, free-draining cactus compost suits all species. Water well and feed regularly during spring and summer; keep the plants completely dry in winter, at a minimum temperature of 15°C (60°F). Exceptions to this advice may be the species that are from more tropical parts, for which a higher temperature should be provided. Propagation is best from seeds.

### P. leucocephalus

From northern Mexico, this is the type species, first named *Pilocereus leucocephalus* by H. Poselger in 1853 and later *Cephalocereus* by Britton and Rose in 1909. A tall species, 3–5 m (10 ft–16 ft 6 in) high in the wild, freely branching from the base to form quite compact clumps. Stems are bluish-green becoming dark green, with about 12 low ribs bearing white woolly areoles, each producing about 10 yellowish-brown spines 2 cm ($\frac{3}{4}$ in) long. The flowering areoles situated on the sides of the upper part of the stems are about 10 cm (4 in) long and have dense white wool and hairs; the flowers are pinkish-white or pale red.

### P. palmeri

Closely related to the above, this occurs in more north-eastern parts of Mexico. It was recorded as *Cephalocereus palmeri* by Rose in 1909 and described as *Cereus victoriensis* by Vaupel in 1913. It is a well-known species which becomes tree-like in habitat, up to 6 m (20 ft) tall. It branches freely, each branch being 8 cm (3 in) in diameter, and bluish-green in colour. There are 7–9 rounded ribs with areoles covered with long woolly hair, each bearing about 12 spines, up to 3 cm (1$\frac{1}{4}$ in) long. The thick wool forms a dense pseudocephalium near the top of the stems, with much longer blackish spines protruding through the wool. The flowers, about 8 cm (3 in) long, are bell-shaped and red on the outside, with pink inner petals.

### P. nobilis

A West Indian species, with dark green erect stems forming clumps. It has smaller flowers, about 5 cm (2 in) long and almost as wide when fully open, pale pink inner petals, reddish-green on the outside. This species needs a higher temperature in winter and an occasional light spray with tepid water.

### P. fulvilanatus

Previously included by Buining and Brederoo in *Pseudopilocereus*, this is from Minas Gerais in Brazil. It is a tree-like species, to 3 m (10 ft) tall and 10 cm (4 in) or a little more thick, with about 5 ribs, bluish-green in colour. The areoles are brownish and woolly; with the brownish-grey spines they form a pseudocephalium through which the white, 5 cm (2 in) long, flowers emerge.

# PTEROCACTUS

A small genus of tuberous-rooted plants very closely allied to *Opuntia*. It was established by Karl Schumann in 1897 and embraces a few species from south Argentina. The generic name is from the Greek *pteron*, meaning wing, and refers to the winged seeds. Like *Opuntia*, the plants have glochids, as well as small leaves which quickly fall. All species are low-growing, with more or less cylindrical stems; the terminal flowers are almost sunk into the stems. The fruits are dry and contain winged seeds, a feature unknown in any other genus of the Cactaceae. In cultivation they need a sunny, bright position and a very porous compost. A proprietary cactus compost is suitable, provided that it drains quickly and does not retain moisture for any length of time as this can damage the thick tuberous rootstock. Feeding is beneficial; three or four times during the growing season is sufficient. Water in moderation at all times; it is important that the plants dry out between applications. Minimum temperature in winter should be 7°C (45°F), when the plants need totally dry conditions. Propagation is from seeds or cuttings.

### P. tuberosus

Also named *P. kuntzei*, this is the type species, from Mendoza. The specific name was given by Pfeiffer when in 1837 he first described the plant as *Opuntia tuberosa*. It has a large thick taproot, about 12 cm (4$\frac{3}{4}$ in) long and 8 cm (3 in) thick, from which develop purplish-brown stems up to 40 cm (16 in) long and about 1 cm ($\frac{3}{8}$ in) thick. Areoles are numerous and closely set, producing dense clusters of minute spines closely appressed to the stems. The flowers, to 3 cm (1$\frac{1}{4}$ in) long, are yellow, followed by dry fruits containing white winged seeds, about 1 cm ($\frac{3}{8}$ in) in diameter.

### P. fischeri

The species was named by Britton and Rose. From Patagonia, it has a thick rootstock bearing low-growing, spreading stems, somewhat tuberculed, and about 2 cm ($\frac{3}{4}$ in) thick. It has minute leaves and areoles with both radial and central spines, numerous glochids, usually yellowish-brown. The white flowers are borne terminally.

# PTEROCEREUS

A small genus consisting of just two species, with every indication that both of these may become reclassified under *Pachycereus*. It was established by T.B. MacDougall and F. Miranda in 1954. The generic name, from the Greek *pteron*, meaning wing, describes the wing-like ribs which are considered sufficiently characteristic to

segregate these species from genera of other columnar plants. They are both tree-like, with mainly very slender growth, the flowers being borne laterally from towards the terminal ends of the branches. It is endemic to Mexico.

In cultivation they need a bright, and preferably sunny position and a fairly rich cactus compost to which limestone chippings should be added. Water moderately during the growing season, then keep completely dry from late October to early April, at a temperature of 10°C (50°F). Propagation is from seeds or cuttings.

### P. gaumeri

Collected by George Gaumer and named for him by Britton and Rose in 1923 as *Cephalocereus gaumeri*, this was later transferred to Backeberg's short-lived genus, *Anisocereus*. There it remained until the present reclassification took place in 1954. A columnar species which in habitat can reach 6 m (20 ft) in height, although the branches are very thin and slender – only about 6 cm (2½ in) thick. They have 4–8 ribs, wing-like, with felted areoles bearing numerous yellowish-brown spines, 4–9 cm (1½–3½ in) long. The flower-bearing areoles are more closely set, very long, woolly and spiny. The flowers, about 7 cm (2¾ in) long, have slightly scaly tubes; greenish-brown on the outside, with pale greenish-white inner petals, and a long protruding style.

*Pterocactus fischeri*

The other recorded species, *P. lepidanthus*, which was also placed in Backeberg's *Anisocereus*, is from Guatemala. It is quite a tall species, but it differs in so many respects that it seems not to belong to this genus at all.

# QUIABENTIA

This genus was established in 1919 by Britton and Rose for a single species from Bahia, Brazil, where its native name is *quiabento*. There are now 5 recognized species, coming from Bolivia and northern parts of Argentina. They make up one of the so-called primitive groups of the Cactaceae, with some species having thick, fleshy leaves, suggesting forms of *Pereskia*, a genus which once contained the type species, *Q. zehntneri*. They are tree-like or bushy plants with slender, cylindrical stems and branches which frequently develop in whorls; they are brittle and easily fall off. The areoles are fairly large, generally with whitish wool and bearing many glochid-like fine spines. All flowers are in varying shades of red. Plants are not difficult in cultivation, although many remain uncommon. They need a bright, sunny position and a porous cactus compost which should contain lime or limestone chippings in order to simulate the calcareous soil in the native habitats. Let the compost dry out between watering during the growing and flowering season; in winter maintain a temperature of 13°C (55°F) and water just enough to prevent shrivelling. Propagation is by cuttings or by seeds.

### Q. zehntneri

Discovered by Leo Zehntner in 1912 near the Rio Sao Francisco in Bahia, Brazil, and subsequently named in his honour, this is a tall-growing plant, 2–3 m (6 ft 6 in–10 ft) high, with a main spiny trunk-like stem and many widely spreading branches in whorls. They are bright green and very fleshy, with many large areoles bearing whitish wool and spines, and numerous fleshy leaves, oval in shape and 2–4 cm ($\frac{3}{4}$–$1\frac{1}{2}$ in) long. Bright red flowers appear at the tips of the branches; they are about 4 cm ($1\frac{1}{2}$ in) long and 8 cm (3 in) across. The ovary is very slender, but 4 cm ($1\frac{1}{2}$ in) long and covered with leaves and spines.

### Q. pflanzii

From Santa Isabel in Bolivia, this was first described by Vaupel as a species of *Pereskia*, and later transferred to

Below: *Pterocereus gaumeri*; below right: *Quiabentia chacoensis*

*Quiabentia*. It is a tree-like plant of large proportions, in its natural habitat up to 15 m (nearly 50 ft) high. It is similar to the above but more robust, with spreading branches bearing leaves about 4 cm ($1\frac{1}{2}$ in) long and 2 cm ($\frac{3}{4}$ in) wide, and numerous short and slender spines. The flowers, which are rose-pink, are approximately 5 cm (2 in) long.

### Q. chacoensis

From the Chaco Austral in northern Argentina, and discovered and named by Backeberg. This is a slender, tree-like plant with white woolly areoles, spade-like leaves about 7 cm ($2\frac{3}{4}$ in) long, and many spines. The flowers are red. The variety *jujuyensis* differs only a little from the type.

# RATHBUNIA

A small genus established by Britton and Rose in 1909 for two species, both from Mexico. The generic name commemorates Richard Rathbun, the American naturalist. The plants are of columnar habit, but with rather slender stems, often resulting in a somewhat drooping growth; they frequently form quite thick clumps, often developing to tree-like proportions. The flowers usually appear near the top of the stems, and are tubular.

There is a close relationship between the genera *Rathbunia* and *Stenocereus*, and it is possible that the two will, in due course, be brought together under a single generic name.

Plants are not too frequently encountered in cultivation although they are of easy cultivation. They thrive in a bright and sunny position where temperatures do not fall below 10°C (50°F) at any time of the year. An ordinary cactus compost is suitable and careful watering is essential at all times. For successful cultivation it is imperative that they are given a dry dormancy period from November to March. A liquid fertilizer should be given at 4-weekly intervals from May to September. Propagation is by seeds.

### R. alamosensis

The type species, which was earlier recorded by Coulter as *Cereus alamosensis*. Britton and Rose mention two synonyms, *Cereus (Rathbunia) sonorensis* and *Cereus pseudosonorensis*; possibly these specific names have led to the erroneous idea that the genus contains four species instead of two. It grows in tall scrub in parts of Sonora and Sinaloa in Mexico, reaching a height of 3 m (10 ft) and becoming almost tree-like at times. More often it forms thick clumps, the elongated stems are supported and kept semi-erect by the surrounding thickets. The stems are only 8 cm (3 in) thick, with 5–8 ribs, while the areoles

*Rathbunia alamosensis*

bear up to 18 straight whitish radial spines, approximately 4 cm (1½ in) long, and 1–4 thicker centrals, approximately 5 cm (2 in) in length, all spreading. The flowers, which are red, are approximately 10 cm (4 in) long. The tubes are scaly, often spiny or with tufts of felt, expanding at the tips to 3–4 cm (1¼–1½ in) across. The flowers are zygomorphic, with protruding whitish stamens, style and stigma lobes.

### R. kerberi

Earlier described by Schumann as *Cereus kerberi* and later by Gosselin as *Cleistocactus kerberi*, this resembles and may prove to be a variety of *R. alamosensis*. It comes from the vicinity of the volcano of Colima in western Mexico and is a columnar plant about 2 m (6 ft 6 in) high, the stems are only about 10 cm (4 in) thick, and are of more erect habit. There are 4 ribs, deeply crenate, with areoles carrying about 16 spreading, awl-shaped radial spines and 3–4 slightly longer centrals. The flowers, which are approximately 4 cm (1½ in) across, are borne near the tips of the stems; they are funnel-shaped and their tubes are covered with red scales and brownish felt. They are zygomorphic, and have reddish petals, style and stigma lobes, and purplish stamens.

# REBUTIA

This genus, established by Schumann in 1895 acknowledges P. Rebut, a French cactus authority, and has been investigated in recent years by John Donald and the late Albert Buining. It has a close relationship with *Lobivia*, *Echinopsis* and *Sulcorebutia* and it is not unlikely that future research will see a merger of one or other of these genera. The numerous recognized species are all of South American origin; whether or not the many names do indeed constitute individually distinct species remains in doubt. It is a genus of colourful and easily flowered plants, in the main of easy culture. They are small plants, but the rounded stems usually branch freely from the base and quickly form attractive clusters; these, with their obvious desire to flower, provide splendid displays of colour during spring and early summer. The small rounded bodies are spirally arranged, with numerous warts or tubercles, from the tips of which the areoles

appear. Mostly, they are densely spined; the flowers, in varied colour displays of white, yellow, orange, pink and brilliant red, appear from areoles set towards the base of the stems, and last for several days.

All species require a very nutritious soil; it must be permeable, and most commercially produced cactus composts are suitable. Alternatively, make up a mixture of one part each of loam, sterilized decomposed humus and shredded peat, with two parts of washed gritty sand. They thrive in sun or semi-shade, the latter possibly preferable; water freely throughout the growing season, but keep relatively dry during dormancy from November to March, with a minimum temperature of 10°C (50°F). Propagation is from seeds or offsets.

Only a comparative few species of the many that deserve mention are described here, but all of them belong to one of the most fascinating groups of cacti.

### R. muscula

At one time known as *Aylostera muscula*, this comes from Bolivia in the region of Tarija, an area rich in species

*Rebutia muscula*

of this genus. *R. muscula* was named by Ritter and P. Thiele and is one of the best representatives of the orange-flowering species. It is a clustering plant with rounded stems which tend to elongate slightly with age. Many spines, up to 50, are borne from each areole; all are white, about 2 mm ($\frac{1}{10}$ in) long, and almost obliterate the green body. The flowers are about 3 cm ($1\frac{1}{4}$ in) long and wide, their beauty enhanced by the style and stamens.

### R. spegazziniana
From the Salta region of north Argentina, where it flourishes on low mountain slopes, the species was described by Backeberg and named to commemorate Carlos Spegazzini. Individual stems are about 10 cm (4 in) long and 4 cm ($1\frac{1}{2}$ in) thick, forming an almost complete globe. It clusters freely and quickly forms substantial clumps. The areoles are woolly, bearing about 14 whitish, short radial spines and 3–5 even shorter central spines tipped with brown. Flowers are rich vermilion, about 3 cm ($1\frac{1}{4}$ in) long and wide, with white style.

*Rebutia marsoneri*

### R. marsoneri
From Jujuy, Argentina, and described by Werdemann, this is generally a clustering plant, although occasionally it tends to remain solitary. It is well armed with spines, mostly quite small, but sometimes more than 1 cm ($\frac{3}{4}$ in) long. The closed buds promise red flowers, but they nevertheless open to bright yellow and are 3 cm ($1\frac{1}{4}$ in) wide.

### R. heliosa
Discovered and described by Walter Rausch, this comes from the Tarija region of Bolivia and is one of the most unusual species yet found. Although it occasionally remains solitary, it usually develops large clusters, each small body spirally covered with numerous tubercles which in turn bear about 25 very fine, white radial spines in a comb-like formation. It is this feature which captures the imagination of cactus enthusiasts, and since the species was introduced in 1970, it remains one

of the most sought-after of cacti. The flowers are about 5 cm (2 in) long and 4 cm (1½ in) across at the tips, deep orange on the upper part of the petals, yellowish-orange below, and with a white throat; the arrangement of both style and stamens adds to the charm.

### R. perplexa

A perplexing species and considerable research preceded the final, correct naming by John Donald. This, too, is from Tarija in Bolivia. The small greyish-green bodies form dense clusters, each covered with a rib-like formation bearing short, yellowish-white radial spines from small yellow-brown areoles. The flowers, which are narrowly trumpet-shaped and about 4 cm (1½ in) long and 3 cm (1¼ in) wide at the tips, are bright lilac-pink in colour and slightly paler pink on the interior of the flowers.

# RHIPSALIDOPSIS

This genus was established by Britton and Rose in 1923, and at the time considered to be monotypic. Subsequently a species of *Schlumbergera* was transferred to *Rhipsalidopsis*, and these two remain the currently recognized members of the genus. The plants can be quite

*Rebutia heliosa*

bushy, with erect or semi-erect growth, or, as often happens in maturity, they become pendulous. Both species are epiphytic and native to forested areas of southern Brazil.

These plants are easy to grow and are popular house plants. They need bright but filtered light, away from direct sun, and an acid cactus compost enriched with leaf-mould and with gritty sand added for improved drainage. Water freely during the flowering and growing season, but keep the compost barely moist during the winter resting period, when a minimum temperature of 10°C (50°F) should be maintained. The plants produce flowers so prolifically that they need a fortnightly liquid feed from spring until late autumn. Propagate from cuttings.

### R. gaertneri

This, the well-known Easter cactus, was originally described as *Epiphyllum gaertneri*, and was later included in *Phyllocactus*, *Epiphyllopsis* and *Schlumbergera* before assuming its present name. The flat joints can measure 4–7 cm (1½–2½ in) long and up to 2.5 cm (1 in) across; they are oval or oval-elongated in shape, with 3–5 tubercles on either side where the areoles, which may each bear one or two bristles, are sited. The joints are truncated at the tips, where another bristly areole is situated. The flowers are borne from the tips of the terminal joints.

*Rebutia perplexa*

They are scarlet in colour, perfectly symmetrical in shape, 4–5 cm ($1\frac{1}{2}$–2 in) wide and about 7 cm ($2\frac{2}{4}$ in) long, and are carried on short tubes; the stamens are red and the slightly longer style is white with outward spreading, creamy-white stigma lobes. The fruits are oval, about 1 cm ($\frac{3}{8}$ in) long and angled. This is primarily an April-flowering species, with the fruits showing their reddish colouring in July.

### R. rosea

First described by N.G. von Lagerheim in 1912 as a *Rhipsalis* species and reclassified in 1923, this is as popular a house plant as *R. gaertneri*. The segments or joints are either flat or angled with concave sides, generally reddish in colour and to about 4 cm ($1\frac{1}{2}$ in) long, 1 cm ($\frac{3}{8}$ in) wide. Areoles are located on the edges, often with soft bristles, and flowers appear from a larger areole on the tips of the uppermost joints. The flowers are about 2–4 cm ($\frac{3}{4}$–$1\frac{1}{4}$ in) long and 3 cm ($1\frac{1}{4}$ in) across at the tips, rose-pink or pinkish-white, with pinkish stamens and a style about 1.2 cm ($\frac{1}{2}$ in) long; the three stigma lobes are white.

# RHIPSALIS

It has been said that it would take an exceedingly clever person adequately to describe the many species, varieties and forms included in this genus. Variations in stem growth, even within the same species, have led to confusion and wrong naming. The genus was established in 1788 by Joseph Gäertner, a German botanist with a particular interest in epiphytic plants. The name is from the Greek *rhips*, meaning pliable reeds, and the elongated stems of many species certainly have such an appearance. They are found chiefly in South America and the West Indies, but also occur in Mexico and southern Florida, USA. They are unique among the Cactaceae in being found also in Madagascar, Sri Lanka and tropical parts of East and West Africa. All are epiphytic, growing in the wild attached to branches of rain-forest trees or on moist rock-faces and sometimes sending out aerial roots which enable the plants to cling to the host tree or rock. A few have erect stems, but mainly they have trailing or pendent stems and branches; the stems can be elongated to 1 m (3 ft 3 in) or more in length, or divided into smaller joints or sections. They can be completely cylindrical, angled or flat and leaf-like, hence the problem of adequate descriptions and definitions.

Possibly more than 50 species and forms exist; many are in cultivation and provide attractive plants for the home or greenhouse, generally of easy culture. The flowers are rather small, borne from areoles on the margins of the angular and leaf-like species or from the well-distributed areoles set along the cylindrical stems. All species are best located in a lightly shaded position; most do well in hanging-baskets. An ordinary cactus compost is satisfactory, but added humus in the form of decomposed leaf-mould is an impetus for plants to grow well, and to produce their attractive flowers and berry-like fruits, the latter justifying the common name of mistletoe cactus. Water should be given freely during the growing season and from autumn only enough to prevent the plants from shrivelling. In winter keep the plants at a minimum temperature of 10°C (50°F). Propagate from cuttings in summer.

### R. cereuscula

From Brazil, and described by Haworth, this is one of the best known species. The stems can reach 1 m (3 ft 3 in) or more in length, often producing smaller branches arranged in whorls at their tips. The whitish flowers appear from areoles along the slender cylindrical branches.

### R. cassutha

The type species, described by Gäertner, has cylindrical stems and branches often bedecked with a few bristles. The flowers are greenish-white or creamy-yellow and produced in abundance.

### R. mesembryanthemoides

From Brazil, and again described by Haworth, this has longish stems covered from base to tip with short thick cylindrical joints, about 1.5 cm ($\frac{5}{8}$ in) long. They have woolly areoles with a few bristles; pale pinkish-white flowers, about 1 cm ($\frac{3}{8}$ in) wide, precede the white, or sometimes pinkish, fruits.

### R. pachyptera

Also from Brazil, and introduced by Pfeiffer, this is a semi-erect plant with angular stems from which leaf-like joints develop. Stems are dark green in colour, sometimes edged with red, and about 15 cm (6 in) long and 8 cm (3 in) broad. One to three flowers emerge from the areoles set at intervals along the margins; they are yellow, or sometimes tinged with red.

### R. crispimarginata

A more unusual species, described by A. Loefgren, this is from Rio de Janeiro. The pure white flowers, 1 cm ($\frac{3}{8}$ in) or a little longer, are followed by pinkish-white fruits. The flattened, leaf-like joints have decidedly wavy margins.

### R. pentaptera

Found in Uruguay and parts of southern Brazil, and introduced by Pfeiffer, this represents those species with cylindrical joints but possessing rib-like angles along their length; these joints sometimes form in whorls from along the semi-erect stems. Flowers are white, and appear from the areoles set in notches along the ribs.

# RHODOCACTUS

This genus of bushy, leafy plants was proposed by Berger and subsequently established by F.M. Knuth in 1935, when it was segregated from its close ally *Pereskia*. It is debatable if that separation is justified, and it is likely that they will become united again. The generic name is from the Greek *rhodon*, referring to the rose-like flowers that adorn all species of the genus. Possibly about 10 species can be recorded in *Rhodocactus*, each having the botanical qualification of the ovary being central to inferior; in this they truly differ from the Pereskias. In a sense they resemble rose bushes rather than cacti as stem and branch growth is scarcely succulent and becomes quite woody in maturity; however, the plants have areoles, which are usually quite prominent, even woolly, and these carry spines and leaves that are thick and fleshy and usually quite sizable. The foliage is persistent, not deciduous, although many leaves may fall during the period of dormancy. It is native to the West Indies and Mexico, down as far as northerly parts of Argentina.

The plants require a warm, slightly shaded position, and a rich acid compost. If they are grown in pots, they must be watered freely in summer and the soil kept just moist in winter; if bedded out in a greenhouse, watering can be continued throughout the year, always in moderation and never permitting too wet conditions. Temperature should be kept at about 15°C (60°F) as a minimum. Propagation is relatively easy from cuttings taken in early summer, allowed to callus for a few days and then inserted in a mixture of equal parts peat and sand; ideally they should be kept in a propagation unit with bottom heat of about 21°C (70°F). After rooting, plant the cuttings in a growing compost consisting of equal parts sterilized loam, shredded peat, decomposed leaf-mould and very sharp gritty sand. Seeds are rarely available.

### R. bleo

Named as *Cactus bleo* by Humboldt, Bonpland and Knuth in 1823, as *Pereskia bleo* by de Candolle in 1828 and subsequently included under *Rhodocactus* by F.M. Knuth, this is found in Panama and Colombia. It develops into a tall bushy, almost tree-like plant which in the wild may attain 7 m (23 ft) in height. It forms a thick trunk, about 10 cm (4 in) in diameter with many branches, bearing areoles from which appear 5–8 black spines and the elongated fleshy leaves, 20 cm (8 in) or more long. The flowers are rose-red, on short stalks; they are mainly borne in small clusters of 2–4 flowers each about 7 cm ($2\frac{3}{4}$ in) across.

### R. grandifolia

Haworth named this a *Pereskia* in 1819, but it was also recorded as *Cactus grandiflora* in 1822; and now sometimes referred to as *R. grandiflora* rather than *R. grandifolia*. It is native to Brazil and probably also the West Indies. A tree-like plant up to 5 m (16 ft 6 in) high with a 10 cm (4 in) thick spiny trunk, it has many branches with areoles each bearing one or two spines and one short-stalked leaf about 15 cm (6 in) long. Flowers appear, several together, at the tips of the branches; each is about 4 cm ($1\frac{1}{2}$ in) wide, pink or in slightly deeper shades, occasionally white. Fruits are pear-shaped containing many black seeds.

# SAMAIPATICEREUS

A small genus, which includes one or two species, probably synonymous with each other. It was established by M. Cardenas, the Bolivian botanist, in 1952; the genus *Yungasocereus* appears to be synonymous with *Samaipaticereus*. The generic name comes from the Bolivian township of Samaipata. The plants are tree-like, with stout trunks and spreading branches; the flowers are comparatively small and nocturnal. Plants are uncommon in cultivation, but when available prove to be relatively easy to grow successfully. A rich open compost is essential, with regular watering during spring and summer, allowing for a definite dry-out period between each application; feed with a liquid fertilizer every 4 weeks from June to October. Keep the compost completely dry during the winter dormancy, at a minimum temperature of 10°C (50°F). Propagation is best by seeds sown early in the year.

### S. corroanus

The type species is from the Bolivian region of Florida (El Puente de Samaipata). It is a columnar plant with tree-like growth, the trunk being about 15 cm (6 in) in diameter and reaching more than 3 m (10 ft) in height. The branches are more slender, about 5 cm (2 in) thick

and dull green in colour, each with 4–6 ribs, the areoles bearing about 5 short, sometimes curled radial spines of pale brown or greyish-white. The white flowers are borne laterally; they are about 5 cm (2 in) long and brown, rather woolly, scaly or bristly on the outside. Another species, *S. inquisivensis*, is probably synonymous, but is said to be of slightly taller growth, with branches having more ribs and longer spines. Flowers are identical.

# SCHLUMBERGERA

This genus has undergone many changes during more recent years when species have been added and others removed. The name was provided by Charles Lemaire in 1858 and honours Frederick Schlumberger, a noted plantsman of his day. At that time only two species were included and one of these has now been reclassified under *Rhipsalidopsis*. The genus *Zygocactus*, after a degree of controversy, was reclassified as *Schlumbergera* by David Hunt in 1969, together with *Epiphyllanthus* with its few of the species whose small stem segments resemble those of *Opuntia*. The genus now includes 5–7 species (the number varying according to the particular authority) and numerous hybrids of varying colours, commonly referred to as Christmas cacti. All species are epiphytes, growing in trees or among rocks where plenty of humus abounds. The stems are divided into small segments, or joints, and growth is usually of pendent habit, although more erect stems are apparent in a few of the species.

The plants are easy to grow and bring into flower. Like other epiphytes they do best in a position with bright but filtered light, out of direct sun; in summer they appreciate a good degree of humidity. An acid cactus compost, with added leaf-mould, is suitable, and it should be porous. Water should be given freely from spring to autumn, moderately during the flowering season from late autumn through to spring. Thereafter, keep the plants just moist during the brief resting period. The ideal winter temperature should not fall below 10°C (50°F). Feed every 3–4 weeks during the growing season and until flower buds have formed. Propagation is by stem cuttings taken in summer.

### S. russelliana

The species was introduced into Britain by G. Gardner in 1839 and named by him *Cereus russellianus*, in honour of the then Duke of Bedford. After several renamings it was transferred to the present genus by Britton and Rose in 1913. It is a tree-growing epiphyte from the Organ Mountains in eastern Brazil, with stems and branches attaining 30 cm (1 ft) in length, which are comprised of a number of small short and flat joints,

*Schlumbergera opuntioides*

each 2 cm ($\frac{3}{4}$ in) or a little more in length and rarely more than 1 cm ($\frac{3}{8}$ in) wide, slightly notched on both edges, with tiny areoles each carrying one or two bristles. The flowers are borne terminally, from late winter until spring; they are about 5 cm (2 in) long and 4 cm (1$\frac{1}{2}$ in) across, fairly symmetrical in shape and reddish-purple in colour, with a 4-angled ovary and a straight tube; stamens are numerous, some arranged on the ovary, the rest inserted in the tube; the style is slender and purple.

### S. truncata

Originally described in 1819 by Haworth, as *Epiphyllum truncatum*, this was reclassified as a *Zygocactus* by Schumann in 1890. It is from the mountain forest around Rio de Janeiro in eastern Brazil; stems and branches are pendent, the branches consisting of flat joints 3–4 cm (1$\frac{1}{4}$–1$\frac{1}{2}$ in) long and about 2 cm ($\frac{3}{4}$ in) wide, with two prominent teeth on either side and two at the tips. Flowers appear during November and December from the areoles at the tips of the upper segments; they are zygomorphic, 6–8 cm (2$\frac{1}{2}$–3 in) long and pink to violet-red in colour. The petals are recurved the stamens white, and the purple style protrudes beyond the petals. Colour variations include var. *delicatus*, with white petals, and var. *crenatus*, with pale violet flowers.

### S. opuntioides

Named because of its miniature *Opuntia*-like joints, this was transferred from *Epiphyllanthus*, a genus created by Berger in 1905 for three species with similar stem sections. It is also known as *S. obovatus*. The pleasing characteristic of the species is the unusual thick, flat or semi-cylindrical segments, which are 2–6 cm ($\frac{3}{4}$–2$\frac{1}{4}$ in) long and about 4 mm ($\frac{1}{8}$ in) thick, more or less oblong in shape. Small white areoles cover all sides of the joints; they are slightly felted, with or without very fine spines. Flowers are borne terminally; they are mainly purplish, about 5 cm (2 in) long, zygomorphic with petals partially recurved and reddish-purple stamens exceeding the petals. This is an excellent plant for flowering from early to mid-April; the several branches of linked joints form a semi-erect bushy plant of unique character. It comes from Brazil, like the similar *S. obtusangula* with its longer, more slender but very fleshy joints, and narrower and shorter flowers that are purplish-violet in colour.

### S. orssichiana

The most recent discovery in this genus was found by Countess Beatrix Orssich in the Serra do Mar, north of São Paulo, in Brazil and named in 1978 by Wilhelm Barthlott and A.J.S. McMillan. It is a pendulous plant with several branches composed of large, flat joints 5–7.5 cm (2–2$\frac{3}{4}$ in) long and 3–4.5 cm (1$\frac{1}{4}$–1$\frac{3}{4}$ in) wide, with slightly reddish margins with two or three areoles set above pronounced teeth. The flowers are zygomorphic, about 9 cm (3½ in) long and equally wide when fully open; the petals are primarily white, edged with magenta at the tips, stamens and style, which is 5–6 cm (2–2½ in) long. The filaments are white with deep yellow anthers, the style carmine with 6–8 stigma lobes. It is unusual in that it flowers in both winter and summer.

A great many hybrids and cultivars have been introduced, ranging in colour from white, yellow and orange to shades of red and purple; the majority are winter flowering. Recommended cultivars include 'Adda Abendroth', like *S. orssichiana* but smaller – perhaps an undescribed species; 'Bridgesii' ('Buckleyi'), the common Christmas cactus, a hybrid between *S. truncata* and *S. russelliana*, with carmine flowers; 'Lilac Beauty', shiny carmine-red petals shading to a whitish throat; 'Rudolf Zenneck', a German hybrid with waxy-orange flowers; 'Gold Charm', one of the first ever yellow hybrids; 'Westland', a Dutch hybrid with bright orange petals and white throat; 'Christmas Cheer', which is similar to 'Westland' but with larger flowers; 'Wintermärchen', which is a German hybrid, with pale whitish-pink flowers; and 'Zara', which has orange-red petals and whitish throat.

# SCLEROCACTUS

This is another confused genus, established by Britton and Rose in 1922 to contain just two species. The name is from the Greek *scler*, meaning hard or cruel, and probably refers to the vicious spination of certain species. It has a close relationship with *Ferocactus*, and certain species have already been reclassified within that genus, though they may well be returned. According to some authorities, the genus should be referred to *Pediocactus*, but there is also a close affinity with *Ancistrocactus*, *Echinomastus* and *Homalocephala*, and the future might well see a merger of some or all of these genera with *Sclerocactus*. The plants are usually solitary, rarely clustering, the spines are outstanding, mainly long and twisted, and many in number. Flowers are more or less bell-shaped and appearing from near the top of the plant bodies. The species are native to Arizona, California, Utah and Colorado. Particular care is required to grow them successfully; they need a truly bright and sunny position and a rich compost with plenty of decomposed humus and ample mineral content. Water in moderation through spring and summer, allowing for brief drying-out of the compost between applications; feed 3–4 times during this period, and keep the plants dry from October to March, at a minimum temperature of 7°C (45°F). Propagation is from seeds.

## S. whipplei

From Colorado, it was named *Echinocactus whipplei* by Engelmann and Bigelow in 1856 and referred to its present genus by Britton and Rose. It is mainly solitary, or forms small clusters, 20 cm (8 in) tall and 8 cm (3 in) or more wide, with white wool in the crown. There are 13–15 prominent and tuberculate ribs, arranged spirally towards the tops. The areoles are set well apart with 7–11 white or brownish-black radial spines, spreading horizontally to 2 cm (¾ in) long, and 4 hooked centrals about 3 cm (1¼ in) long. Flowers, 5 cm (2 in) long, appear from the upper areoles; they are pink to purple, rarely white.

## S. polyancistrus

The type species, it is found in California and Nevada. It is a solitary plant, 20 cm (8 in) tall and 10 cm (4 in) in diameter, with 13–17 slightly tuberculate ribs with rounded, yellowish-brown areoles. Each bears about 20 radial spines, 4.5 cm (1¾ in) long, and 10 centrals which may be straight or curved, 7–12 cm (2¾–4¾ in) in length, yellowish-brown to purplish-brown. Flowers are purplish-red with yellowish-red inner petals, 5–6 cm (2–2½ in) or more long.

# SELENICEREUS

This genus contains one of the 22 original species placed in *Cactus* by Linnaeus in 1753. It was *Cactus grandiflorus*, now the type species of *Selenicereus*. The generic name is from the Greek *selene*, meaning moon, and refers, perhaps, to the nocturnal flowers. The name has been attributed to Berger, and was, in any case, confirmed by Britton and Rose in 1909. The genus includes some 20 distinctive species, including those previously contained within *Mediocactus*, all of which climb or trail by means of long aerial roots and are associated with forested regions. They are found from Texas in the south of the USA, in parts of Mexico, throughout much of Central and South America to Argentina and Uruguay, and in the West Indies. The climbing habit is valid for all; they generally clamber up tall trees or, in certain species, spread in haphazard fashion over shady rock faces. They have slender stems carrying many small or large spines; nocturnal flowers are often gigantic although a few have smaller blooms. Without exception they are easy to cultivate, though they do not flower until well established. Use a proprietary cactus compost, or a soil-less compost to which a third of the bulk in sharp gritty sand has been added. Pot firmly and place in a bright position, out of direct sun, where the branches can climb and spread. Water regularly throughout the growing season, giving a liquid fertilizer every 3–4 weeks. In winter keep the compost almost dry, but maintain a minimum temperature of 13°C (55°F). Propagation is by cuttings.

## S. grandiflorus

A variable species and a number of botanical varieties are recorded. They are mainly native to the West Indies, but records suggest that Mexico may also be the habitat of one or two of them. The long stems and branches are 3 cm ($1\frac{1}{4}$ in) thick and have up to 8 ribs with yellowish-white, woolly areoles bearing about 10 needle-like spines. Flowers are white or creamy-white; with the elongated tube they can measure up to 30 cm (1 ft) in length and when fully open 20 cm (8 in) across. They have a scent of vanilla and open towards evening only to close by mid-morning the following day. The beauty and attraction of the flowers has earned the species the name of queen of the night, which perhaps it should rightfully share with others of the genus.

## S. macdonaldiae

From Uruguay and Argentina, this species has even larger flowers, expanding widely and invariably more than 30 cm (1 ft) long, but without fragrance. The petals are creamy-white, the sepals orange-purple and widely reflexed. It is a much-branching plant, with glossy-green stems having 5–7 ribs marked with prominent, flattened tubercles set at intervals of about 4 cm ($1\frac{1}{2}$ in). Rooted sections of the stems make excellent grafting stock for species of *Schlumbergera*.

## S. murrilli

From Yucatan in Mexico, this is an epiphytic species found by W.A. Murrill and named for him by Britton and Rose. It has very slender, vine-like growth which can trail to 6 m (20 ft) or more, the stems being only about 1 cm ($\frac{3}{8}$ in) thick. Many aerial roots develop along the dark green branches which are set with about 8 low purplish ribs bearing well-spaced areoles each with a few minute spines. The flowers, 15 cm (6 in) long, are borne on purple-green, scaly tubes; the petals are cup-shaped and pure white, the sepals are pale purple. This is one of the rarer species, but once obtained it is easy in cultivation.

# SETIECHINOPSIS

A monotypic genus established in 1940 by De Haas for an obviously unique plant, even though it is closely related to a species of *Echinopsis*. The generic name is from the Latin *seta*, meaning bristle, and refers to the very long floral tube which has bristle-like scales. Plants are short, columnar and rarely exceed 15 cm (6 in) in height; they generally remain solitary. They are of very easy culture, requiring a bright position ideally with full sun for several hours each day. An ordinary cactus compost will ensure successful development of both growth and flowers. Water in moderation throughout spring and

*Setiechinopsis mirabilis*

summer and, if a minimum winter temperature of 13°C (55°F) can be maintained, give just sufficient water to prevent the fleshy rootstock from drying out completely. Keep the plants dry if they are overwintered at lower temperatures. Apply a weak liquid fertilizer at intervals of 3–4 weeks during the growing season. Propagate by seeds.

## S. mirabilis

First mentioned by Spegazzini in 1905, when it was described as an *Echinopsis*; it was later transferred to *Arthrocereus* before being reclassified within *Setiechinopsis*. It seems probable that present-day taxonomists will reunite this unusual plant with *Echinopsis*. It is native to Santiago del Estero in Argentina where it is known as Flor de la Oración, meaning flower of prayer, possibly because the rather charming flowers open in the evening at the hour of prayer. The plant is dull bluish-green, 10–15 cm (4–6 in) tall and about 2 cm ($\frac{3}{4}$ in) thick, with 11–12 slightly undulating ribs. The areoles are tiny, bearing 9–14 whitish radial spines and one brown central, all 1.5 cm ($\frac{5}{8}$ in) long. Flowers are pure white and scented, 12 cm ($4\frac{3}{4}$ in) long and opening to 3 cm ($1\frac{1}{4}$ in) or a little more across. The scaly and bristly tube is brownish in colour as are the outer flower segments, while the slender inner petals are white. Flowers appear from the very crown of the plant, followed by large fruits about 4 cm (1½ in) long.

# STENOCEREUS

This is one of several genera that have recently absorbed a number of other well-known groups, including *Machaerocereus* and *Ritterocereus*. It has experienced many changes; when it was first established in 1909 by Riccobono it contained one species only, although it had been used by Berger as a sub-generic name in 1905. With the enlargement of the genus, there are now in the region of 25 species, some from the genera mentioned above, others from the long-established erstwhile *Lemaireocereus* and *Hertrichocereus*. The generic name is from the Greek *stenos*, meaning narrow, and possibly applies to the narrow campanulate flowers that occur on some species. All are columnar plants, some almost tree-like. The rib formation varies considerably from species to species; some have as few as 4 ribs, others up to 20. Flowers appear towards the tops of the stems, some protruding laterally; mostly they are nocturnal. The plants are widespread in habitat, from Mexico and other Central American countries to many of the West Indian islands and to Venezuela. In cultivation, they need a sunny airy position with ample space to enable them to grow successfully. An ordinary, free-draining cactus compost is satisfactory. Water well during spring and summer, then gradually restrict watering to reach complete dryness in winter, at a temperature of 10°C (50°F). Feed at 4-weekly intervals during the growing season. Propagate by seeds sown early in the year.

### S. stellatus

Native to southern Mexico, this is the type species and the first to be included. It was named by Pfeiffer in 1836 as *Cereus stellatus*, later finding itself in *Lemaireocereus*. It is one of the most beautiful of columnar cacti, with bluish-green, sometimes almost reddish stems which in the wild can reach over 2 m (6 ft 6 in) in height; each stem or branch is about 9 cm (3½ in) thick with about 12 ribs, low set and slightly uneven, the areoles appearing in these depressions, about 2 cm (¾ in) apart. Each bears 10–12 greyish-black radial spines, about 2.5 cm (1 in) long, and up to 6 slightly longer centrals. The narrow flowers are borne terminally; they are about 6 cm (2½ in) long, pinkish-red on the outside, with white inner petals. *S. stellatus* is reputed to have edible fruit.

### S. dumortieri

This was described by Scheidweiler as *Cereus dumortieri* in 1837 and, before being given its present generic status

by Buxbaum, it was included in both *Lemaireocereus* and *Isolatocereus*. It comes from Oaxaca in Mexico and is a well-known, tree-like species that in the wild can reach 15 m (nearly 50 ft) in height, with a trunk about 30 cm (1 ft) thick. It is a branching species with bluish-green branches having up to 9 acute ribs, with areoles set close together along the edges; they each carry 15–20 radial spines, about 1 cm (⅜ in) long, and a few longer centrals, all pale yellowish in colour. Flowers appear from the sides of the stems, in almost longitudinal lines; they are about 5 cm (2 in) long, with bristly tubes, white inner petals, reddish-brown on the outside.

### S. thurberi

The organ-pipe cactus of Mexico. It was named by Engelmann as *Cereus thurberi* in 1854 and since then has appeared in both *Lemaireocereus* and *Pilocereus* prior to the present reclassification by Buxbaum. The species has many erect branches ascending from the base and reaching to 7 m (23 ft) high in the wild. Each stem has 12–19 ribs, somewhat rounded at the edges and with large brown-felted areoles, from which appear 8–10 black-brown radial spines, about 1 cm (⅜ in) long, and one to three centrals, 2.5 cm (1 in) in length. The flowers appear from the tips of the branches, each is about 7 cm (2¾ in) long, the outer petals reddish, the inner petals purplish-pink with white margins. The fruits are about 7 cm (2¾ in) in diameter and become more or less spineless as they ripen; they are said to be edible and relished by the Seri Indians of Sonora.

### S. eruca

Long known as *Machaeocereus eruca*, the creeping devil, this is one of those cacti which once seen is never forgotten. It occurs only in Baja California, including Magdalena Island. It was originally included in *Cereus* by Brandegee, then transferred first to *Machaerocereus* by Britton and Rose and finally in 1979 to *Stenocereus* by A.C. Gibson and K.E. Horak. It is a prostrate plant, literally creeping, with occasional ascending short branches which, in turn, become prostrate. The thick stems, 8 cm (3 in) or more wide, can creep for 3 m (10 ft) or more, throwing down roots as they travel along, sometimes dying off at one end only to grow on at the other. Each stem has 12 ribs with large areoles carrying about 20 radial spines, reddish becoming grey, and one central spine about 3 cm (1¼ in) long. The flowers are whitish and up to 14 cm (5½ in) long.

# STEPHANOCEREUS

A genus established for a single species by A. Berger in 1926. The name comes from the Greek *stephanos*, meaning crown or corona, a feature of considerable promi-

Above: *Stenocereus eruca*; right: *Stenocereus thurberi*

nence when plants reach maturity. This crown is in the form of a cephalium borne at the apex of the stem through which it continues to grow so that another terminal cephalium forms during the following season. This peculiar characteristic suggests a close affinity with species of *Arrojadoa*; it is also similar in other respects to species of *Pilosocereus*.

It is a fairly easy plant in cultivation; given a really bright and sunny position with reasonable warmth throughout the year, quick growth can be registered. Provide an enriched, mineral-based compost and water carefully, with brief intervals of drying out during the spring and summer months; add liquid fertilizer to the water every 6 weeks or so. Keep the plant quite dry in winter, at a minimum temperature of 10°C (50°F). Propagation is by seeds.

### S. leucostele
From southerly parts of Bahia in Brazil where the terrain is frequently very arid. It is a tall erect plant of columnar growth which in habitat reaches 3 m (10 ft) in height. It is solitary, but sometimes branches from the base. Each stem is about 10 cm (4 in) thick, dull green in colour and with 12 to 18 ribs. Initially named *Cereus leucostele* by Gürke in 1908, it was reclassified as

*Cephalocereus* by Britton and Rose in 1922. The spination is the distinctive feature, apparent along the length of the stems and within the cephalium. Areoles are set at intervals of about 1 cm ($\frac{3}{8}$ in); each has more than 20 greyish-white radial spines, 1.5 cm ($\frac{5}{8}$ in) long, and one or two centrals, 5 cm (2 in) in length; they are surrounded by a dense mass of woolly hairs. The terminal cephalium consists of a thick crown of white wool and yellowish bristles; from here appear the nocturnal flowers, which are approximately 6 cm ($2\frac{1}{2}$ in) long, with yellow floral tubes and white petals. With the next growing season, the stem emerges through the cephalium, leaving a ring of wool and bristles which persists; in due course another cephalium forms on top of the new growth.

# STETSONIA

A genus of columnar plants established by Britton and Rose in 1920 for just one species. The plants are found only in Argentina, where they are a conspicuous feature in the northwestern deserts. In their natural habitat, they can develop tree-like proportions, but they rarely exceed about 1 m (3 ft 3 in) when grown in cultivation. The species is quite well known in Europe; it grows readily from seeds and quickly creates a pleasing plant for the home or greenhouse. A very bright and sunny position is advisable; to an ordinary cactus compost a sprinkling of limestone chippings may be added to advantage. Water should be given freely during spring and summer, but keep the plant dry throughout winter; the temperature should not fall below a minimum of 10°C (50°F).

### S. coryne

Previously recorded by Salm-Dyck as *Cereus coryne*, this can become tree-like in the wild, branching thickly from a short trunk about 40 cm (16 in) in diameter and attaining 5–8 m (16 ft 6 in–26 ft) in height. The stems are about 10 cm (4 in) thick, bluish-green in colour, with 8–9 ribs, the margins slightly crenate. Areoles are set below arrow-shaped grooves and carry 7–9 yellowish-white radial spines, about 3 cm ($1\frac{1}{4}$ in) long, and a single, 8 cm (3 in) long central which, like the radials, becomes almost black. Flowers are nocturnal, 12–15 cm ($4\frac{1}{2}$–6 in) long, greenish on the outside, with white inner petals, borne on long scaly tubes.

# STROMBOCACTUS

The genus was established by Britton and Rose in 1922 and *Mammillaria disciformis* was chosen to be the type – and only – species. The generic name is taken from the

*Strombocactus disciformis*

Greek *strombos*, meaning top (or spinning top) and refers to the unusual shape of the plant. It is closely allied to *Turbinicarpus* (which is now considered synonymous with *Neolloydia*) but differs in the fruit and seeds. A more or less compressed globular plant dominated by large tubercles, it is known only from Hidalgo in Mexico where it grows in rocky terrain, usually in narrow crevices. While it remains rather rare in cultivation, it is not necessarily a difficult plant to grow given the sunniest position possible. It requires a porous calcareous compost enriched with decomposed leaf-mould. A winter temperature of at least 10°C (50°F) helps to ensure a healthy growing plant. Water carefully in summer, but keep totally dry in winter. Propagate by seeds sown in late winter or early spring.

### S. disciformis

This is a unique cactus, rather flattened and globular, always solitary and usually about 7 cm ($2\frac{3}{4}$ in) in diameter, though recorded as being much larger. The closely arranged, greyish-green rhomboid tubercles, each 1 cm ($\frac{3}{8}$ in) or a little more wide, cover the plant completely. They are slightly raised in the centre and each carries a whitish areole from which a few whitish, bristly spines appear, soon to fall away. The funnel-shaped flowers are about 4 cm ($1\frac{1}{2}$ in) across when fully open, white or yellowish with similarly coloured style and stamens. They are borne in summer and sometimes again in mid-autumn. The fruits are tiny, about 8 mm ($\frac{3}{10}$ in) long, and greenish becoming brown.

# STROPHOCACTUS

This genus contains but a single species, but that is one of the most unusual cacti ever found. It is native to the Brazilian Amazonas in an area near Manaus where it is invariably swampy and the forests are frequently inundated. A true epiphyte with elongated, flattened, stems and branches, it uses numerous aerial roots to fasten itself closely to tree trunks and twine around branches, often to several metres in length. The generic name was established by Britton and Rose in 1913, when it was realized that the inclusion of the plant in *Cereus* was inappropriate. The name aptly describes the characteristic twisting and climbing habit and comes from the Greek *strophos*, meaning turning. The species is undoubtedly the least common cactus to be found in collections; only rarely is it encountered and then as a plant for the specialist. Its cultural needs are demanding: the soil must be acid and reasonably porous, the position in filtered light, not full sun, and it must be provided with means for climbing, as it is inclined to rot if left pendent. A minimum temperature of 18°C (65°F), preferably a little higher, is essential in winter, and it can soar much higher

in summer. High humidity is also essential, with good circulation of air; regular spraying throughout the year and frequent watering and feeding throughout the warmest months are other necessary provisions. Propagate by cuttings in summer.

Controversy persists as to whether *Strophocactus* should be included in *Selenicereus*, with which there is indeed a close affinity. On the other hand, many authorities consider that this extraordinary plant is a link between *Epiphyllum* and the more cereoid cacti and that its monotypic status should, therefore, continue to be upheld.

### S. wittii

Named after N.H. Witt of Manaus, the plant's discoverer, it has slender leaf-like stems, often 8 cm (3 in) or more wide, the margins of which are edged with closely-set areoles from which appear numerous brownish-yellow, short spines, rarely more than 1 cm ($\frac{3}{8}$ in) long. The dark-green, sometimes reddish-green colouring of the branches contrasts with the lighter shade of the spination. Flowers are nocturnal; they are funnel-shaped, with white inner petals and pinkish outer petals borne on long tubes, in all about 25 cm

*Strophocactus wittii*

(10 in) long. The spiny fruits are egg-shaped, about 3 cm (1¼ in) long, pale green at first but turning pink; they contain many black angular seeds.

# SULCOREBUTIA

A genus introduced by Backeberg in 1951 to contain just one species. Since that time repeated discoveries have meant that 40 or more species have been assigned to the genus. The name is from the Greek *sulcus*, meaning furrow, and refers to the furrows or grooves that occur between the somewhat tuberculate ribs. All species recorded to date are from Bolivia; they have a close relationship with other South American genera, especially *Rebutia*. Once again taxonomists deliberate precisely where *Sulcorebutia*, as a genus, belongs; current trends suggest that it could be merged with *Rebutia*, together with *Weingartia*. Alternatively there is a possible link to *Lobivia*, and from that to *Echinopsis*. All species are globular or slightly elongated, the individual stems are always small. They have a clustering habit, forming offsets quite freely from near the base of the stems, which invariably have many ribs, generally spirally arranged, and tuberculate with quite long areoles bearing spines sometimes in comb-like formations. Flowers are borne from the sides, not the crown, and have a variety of colour forms unequalled elsewhere in the Cactaceae.

The species are, in the main, high-altitude plants and need an extremely bright and sunny position which should also afford good ventilation. A rich porous soil is essential, especially for those species with taproots. Careful watering procedures are important. From early spring until late June, water regularly but in moderation; apply more freely until after flowering is finished, then gradually reduce watering until late October, when the plants will enter their winter rest. During the period of dormancy they should be kept at a minimum temperature of 10°C (50°F). A dilute liquid fertilizer can be added to the watering at monthly intervals from early April until late September. Propagation is by careful removal of offsets, or by seeds.

### S. steinbachii

The type species, this was first included in *Rebutia* by Werdemann. It comes from Cochabamba, Bolivia, at altitudes of around 2500 m (approximately 8000 ft). The stems, about 6 cm (2½ in) high and 4 cm (1½ in) wide, form clusters of offsets almost grass-green in colour. There are about 15 tuberculate ribs, set somewhat irregularly and bearing areoles with 6–8 dark-brown, almost black, needle-like radial spines, and one to three centrals, all about 2 cm (¾ in) or slightly more in length. The flowers

*Sulcorebutia totorensis*

*Sulcorebutia rauschii*

are a reddish shade (sometimes reddish-violet), slender and approximately 3.5 cm (1⅜ in) in length and 2 cm (¾ in) across.

### S. totorensis

Another species from the Cochabamba region of Bolivia, this was introduced by Cardenas as *Rebutia*, then reclassified by Ritter as *Sulcorebutia*. The stems are about 6 cm (2½ in) across, rarely more than 2 cm (¾ in) high and dark green in colour, with up to 21 ribs encircling the stem. Areoles bear numerous dark brown spines, chiefly short, but some 2 cm (¾ in) long. The flowers are an attractive, rich purple, and they are approximately 3–4 cm (1¼–1½ in) long.

### S. mizquensis

Again from Cochabamba, this is one of the smaller species, which nevertheless sprouts freely to form cushions. It was introduced and described by Rausch.

The stems are greyish-green in colour, 2.5 cm (1 in) high and 3 cm (1¼ in) wide with about 17 ribs furnished with areoles each bearing 20 whitish-pink and black spines, 4 mm (⅛ in) long, and densely covering the stem. The flowers are about 3 cm (1¼ in) long, pinkish-purple to magenta.

### S. rauschii

From the Chuquisaca area of Bolivia, this is one of the most unusual of the genus. Named for Walter Rausch by G. Frank, it is a remarkable miniature with blackish-green or purplish stems, each about 1.5 cm (⅝ in) high and 2.5 cm (1 in) or slightly more wide. There are about 16 ribs, prominently tubercled, from the tips of which appear 10–11 minute, black radial spines; there are no centrals. The flowers, about 3 cm (1¼ in) long, have glistening magenta-pink petals, fading to pinkish-white in the throat.

### S. canigueralii

Also native to Chuquisaca, and named by Buining and

Donald, this is only up to 1 cm ($\frac{3}{8}$ in) tall and about 2 cm ($\frac{3}{4}$ in) wide, greyish-green in colour, with about 13 ribs. Each areole has about 12 whitish or brownish small radial spines, sometimes a single central, and flowers that are 4 cm ($1\frac{1}{2}$ in) long and wide, reddish orange in colour and becoming deep yellow towards the base of the petals.

# TACINGA

This is one of the more uncommon genera in the *Opuntiae* group. The genus was established in 1919 by Britton and Rose, the name being a near anagram of *caatinga*, the habitat scrub country of northern Brazil, in the region of Bahia where thorn-bush deserts prevail. They are climbing plants with cylindrical, slender stems that branch freely, often spreading to 10–12 m (33–40 ft). Young growth bears leaves, which quickly shrivel and fall. The areoles are brownish and bear a few spines and white glochids, more so on new branches. Only two species are included in the genus; both are nocturnal flowering.

The plants present few problems in cultivation. They revel in full sun and bright light and do well in any proprietary cactus compost with rapid drainage. Although they are drought-resistant, growth is better with regular applications of water during the growing and flowering season; in winter restrict watering to the minimum if temperatures are around 10°C (50°F); below that keep the plants completely dry. Feed every 4 weeks during the summer and propagate by cuttings then.

### T. funalis

This is the type species. It is of slender growth, about 1.5 cm ($\frac{5}{8}$ in) thick and more or less cylindrical in shape; older stems become woody. The new growth is reddish, very hairy, with many or few tiny leaves, and areoles on the lower portion of the branches set with white glochids. The flowers are pale-greenish in colour, about 8 cm (3 in) long, with quite long tubes; they have only a few greenish petals which are prominently recurved but between these and the stamens is a circle of fine hairs; the stamens protruding beyond the hairs, the slender style extending even further, about 4.5 cm ($1\frac{3}{4}$ in) long, creamy-yellow in colour, with 5 green stigma lobes.

### T. zehntneri

First placed in *Opuntia*, and named after its discoverer, this would seem to be the same plant as that described by Backeberg as *T. atropurpurea*, together with a var. *zehntnerioides*. The growth is similar to *T. funalis* in many respects, but the branches rarely exceed 2 m (6 ft 6 in) in length; they are a dullish green, with areoles bearing wool and glochids. Flowers, about 7 cm ($2\frac{1}{2}$ in) long, are purplish or purplish-green in colour, and the fruits are oval in shape, with just a few white seeds. Whether this is simply a variation of the other species is still in doubt.

# THELOCACTUS

This is one of the more colourful genera of the Cactaceae, especially at flowering time. It was given generic status by Britton and Rose in 1922, having previously been used by Schumann as a sub-generic title of *Echinocactus*. The name is from the Greek *thele*, meaning nipple, and is suggestive of the tubercles that are arranged along the ribs. The species, native to central parts of Mexico, have a close akinship to *Ferocactus*, and *Thelocactus bicolor*, one of the most outstanding and impressive species of the genus, has been reclassified as a *Ferocactus*. There is also an affinity with *Mammillaria* and *Coryphantha*, and it is possible that *Thelocactus* forms a bridge between these two important groups. They are medium-sized globular plants with generally a few ribs divided into tubercles; the flowering tubercles near to the crown have a furrow above each, as in the *Coryphantha* species. The flowers are invariably extremely colourful.

*Tacinga funalis*

These plants are amongst the easiest of cacti to grow successfully. Given a position in full sun they will respond with colourful spination and equally beautiful flowers. A rich cactus compost must be provided; from April until late October water in moderation, adding a dilute liquid fertilizer every 3–4 weeks. Keep the plants totally dry for the rest of the year, with a minimum temperature in winter of 10°C (50°F); at other times higher temperatures should prevail. Propagation is by seeds, which produce excellent results quite quickly.

### T. hexaedrophorus

From San Luis Potosí, Mexico, is the type species, earlier recorded by Lemaire as *Echinocactus hexaedrophorus*. The body is about 15 cm (6 in) in diameter, sometimes slightly flattened on top. There are about 12 ribs divided into a series of large angled tubercles tipped with small areoles; these each bearing 6–9 radial spines, about 1.8 cm ($\frac{3}{4}$ in) in length, and sometimes one or more centrals, about 3 cm ($1\frac{1}{4}$ in) long. All the spines have transverse rings which contrast with the reddish-brown spines. Flowers, 6 cm ($2\frac{1}{2}$ in) long, have pinkish-lilac outer segments, white inner petals with toothed tips, yellow stamens and a style with creamy-yellow stigma lobes.

*Thelocactus bicolor* var. *tricolor*

### T. phymatothelos

From central Mexico, this is another transfer from *Echinocactus*, in which it was placed by Poselger in 1885. It is a smaller species, about 5 cm (2 in) high, but up to 10 cm (4 in) in diameter and greyish-green in colour. The stem has 13 ribs divided into somewhat irregular pointed tubercles with sometimes one to three grey-black spreading spines, 2 cm ($\frac{3}{4}$ in) long. The flowers are about 6 cm ($2\frac{1}{2}$ in) long and wide, rose-pink to pale purple.

### T. conothelos

From Tamaulipas, Mexico, this was placed by E.A. von Regel and W. Klein in *Echinocactus* and transferred later to *Thelocactus* by F.M. Knuth. It grows to about 10 cm (4 in) tall and about 7.5 cm ($2\frac{3}{4}$ in) wide, and has about 12 ribs with greyish-green tubercles arranged somewhat spirally. The areoles carry 14–16 radial spines, almost white, and usually 2–4 yellowish centrals. The purple flowers are about 3.5 cm ($1\frac{3}{8}$ in) across when fully open.

### T. (or Ferocactus) bicolor

The best-known species and deservedly popular for its spine colour and flowers. It has many synonyms, including *Echinocactus bicolor*, the name given it by H.G. Galeotti in 1848. The plant, from San Luis Potosí and Durango in Mexico and also found in southern Texas, can vary in height, but is usually about 10 cm (4 in) tall and as much or more in diameter, with 8–13 spirally arranged ribs. The spines are outstanding and consist of 9–18 spreading reddish-white radials, 3 cm ($1\frac{1}{4}$ in) long, and usually 4 straight centrals, 5 cm (2 in) in length. The 6 cm ($2\frac{1}{2}$ in) long flowers are deep purplish-pink, the throats inset with yellow stamens. The variety *bolansis* has exceptionally long, densely arranged white spines, and lilac-purple flowers.

# TRICHOCEREUS

This is one of the best known genera within Cactaceae, but it is in the process of losing its identity to *Echinopsis*, where botanists have now placed it. It was established by Riccobono in 1909 subsequent to being a sub-genus of Berger's *Cereus*. The generic name is from the Greek *thrix*, meaning hair or thread, and refers to the hairy flower areoles. The genera *Leucostele*, *Soehrensia* and others have become synonymous and it would seem that these, too, with many more, will be absorbed within *Echinopsis*. All species are native to South America and are generally columnar, though some are short cylindrical; many branch, others remain solitary, and they are either day- or night-flowering. They are among the easiest of plants to grow and they flower happily in cultivation. A bright sunny position is advisable – in shade the stems tend to etiolate. A proprietary, porous cactus compost is suitable for most species. Water well from April to October, adding a feed to the water every 3–4 weeks. Keep the plants totally dry in winter, at a minimum temperature of 10°C (50°F). Propagation is from cuttings or seeds. Young plants of a number of species have proved excellent as grafting stock for weaker-growing plants of other genera.

### T. macrogonus

From Argentina and Bolivia, named earlier by Salm-Dyck as *Cereus macrogonus*, this has a bluish-green stem about 3 m (10 ft) in height and 9 cm (3¾ in) thick. It has 6–9 low ribs with large areoles bearing 6–9 brown radial spines, 2 cm (¾ in) long, and one to three centrals to 5 cm (2 in). Flowers are nocturnal, 18 cm (7 in) long, and often borne two or three together near the top of the stems; they have scaly, or hairy brown tubes, green outer petals and white inner petals.

### T. bruchii

From Catamarca to Jujuy in Argentina, this is perhaps better known as *Soehrensia bruchii*. It is globular or elongating-cylindrical in shape, 50 cm (20 in) in diameter; the stem has approximately 50 ribs and whitish areoles, which bear 9–14 radial spines and about four centrals. The flowers, which are diurnal, are 5 cm (2 in) across and bright red in colour.

### T. pachanoi

From Ecuador and Peru, this is possibly the most familiar of the genus. It is a tree-like plant 6 m (20 ft) tall and 12 cm (4½ in) thick, bluish-green in colour and sometimes with long spines, though often spineless. The nocturnal flowers are scented, pure white and about 20 cm (8 in) long.

# TURBINICARPUS

This somewhat unusual group of plants was segregated under this generic name by Backeberg and Buxbaum in 1937. The name is derived from the Latin *turbineus*, meaning shaped like a spinning-top, and the Greek *karpos*, which refers to the fruit. The genus is currently being considered for a merger with *Neolloydia* with which there is a degree of affinity. They are small plants, varying considerably in both spination, which can be papery or pectinate, and in the tubercles which cover the plant bodies. The whole genus is very unsatisfactorily defined as it combines 6 species which differ too much in supporting features, some of these have previously been assigned to genera where general descriptions are unclear. The plants raise no particular problem in culti-

Below left: *Trichocereus bruchii*; below: *Turbinicarpus valdezianus*

*Uebelmannia pectinifera*

vation as long as their essential requirements are taken care of; they need a bright position, but out of full sun, and a rich, very porous compost. Water moderately throughout the growing season and keep the plants fairly dry in winter, at a temperature of about 9°C (48°F). Flowering frequently occurs in early spring. Propagation is from seeds early in the year.

### T. lophophoroides
Included previously within both *Strombocactus* and *Toumeya*, *T. lophophoroides* comes from San Luis Potosí in Mexico. This plant is decidedly similar to *Lophophora* in appearance, but is only about 4.5 cm ($1\frac{3}{4}$ in) in diameter, and is greyish-green in colour. The rather flattened tubercles have areoles bearing 2–6 blackish spines, about 1 cm ($\frac{3}{8}$ in) long. The flowers are pale pink or whitish and about 3.5 cm ($1\frac{3}{8}$ in) acros; they appear from the woolly crown.

### T. valdezianus
A delightful miniature from Coahuila in Mexico, this is only about 2.5 cm (1 in) high and wide. It was initially recorded by L. Möeller as *Pelecyphora valdeziana*, the specific name, it is said, being in honour of his mother-in-law. The spirally arranged tubercles have areoles bearing about 30 minute, hair-like, feathery, white radial spines and no centrals. The flowers, which are approximately 2 cm ($\frac{3}{4}$ in) wide, are purplish-white or pale violet; the stamens and style are yellow and the stigma lobes are white.

# UEBELMANNIA

A genus of some 6 species which caused great excitement, they were introduced by Buining in 1967, and plants began to arrive in Europe. The generic name recognizes the cactus grower and nurseryman Werner Uebelmann, who was largely responsible for the expedition that first located these plants and arranged their importation into Europe. Native to Minas Gerais in Brazil, they are more or less globular, sometimes becoming elongated, with many symmetrically arranged ribs, often with closely set areoles and flowers of yellow or greenish-yellow. Without question, they are not the easiest of plants to grow successfully, and in consequence they are often grafted on to more adaptable stock. If grown on their own roots, a very free-draining, rich, acid compost is required, with plenty of added humus. In a sense they enjoy much the same atmospheric conditions as epiphytic cacti; careful watering is essential, and mist-spraying is beneficial. The plants must be kept warm at all times, at never less than 15°C

(60°F); occasional overhead spraying with tepid water is advisable in the winter months. Propagation is by seeds.

### U. gummifera

First described by Backeberg and Voll as *Parodia gummifera*, then adopted by Buining as the type species for this genus. It is a greyish-green, rather globular plant, about 10 cm (4 in) tall and 6 cm (2½ in) wide, with 30 or more narrow ribs set closely together. The areoles bear 2–4 spreading and one downward-pointing radial spine, and one awl-like central, all greyish and tipped brown. Bright-yellow flowers are about 2 cm (¾ in) long and 1.5 cm (⅝ in) wide.

### U. pectinifera

Named by Buining, this is undoubtedly one of the most unusual of cacti. Almost globular at first, the stem elongates to about 50 cm (20 in) tall and 12–15 cm (4½–6 in) in diameter; it is purplish-brown initially but gradually turns to a greyish-purplish-white, emphasized by the minute scales that cover the surface and which become more pronounced as the plant matures. There are 15–18, very acute ribs, the edges totally covered with closely-set areoles bearing several blackish, comb-like central spines, about 1.5 cm (⅝ in) long. There are no radial spines. The flowers are greenish-yellow, 1.5–2 cm (⅝–¾ in) long and a little more than 1 cm (⅜ in) wide. Fruits are relatively large, bright red in colour and berry-like. The variety *pseudopectinifera* is greener in colour and has less acute ribs and less confluent areoles, but longer spines, which are not comblike. The flowers are similar.

# WEBERBAUREOCEREUS

This genus was established by Backeberg in 1942 and commemorates August Weberbauer, an eminent cactologist who died in 1948. There is a close relationship with *Haageocereus* and *Trichocereus* (now included in *Echinopsis*); *Rauhocereus*, is considered synonymous. All the 5–6 species are native to Peru, mostly from the mountainous countryside of the south. They are of erect columnar growth, some rather tree-like, others in tall, bushy clumps, but all have many low, rounded ribs, numerous spines and interesting and unusual flowers. Cultivation is straightforward. Use a carefully prepared compost of equal parts of sterilized loam, decomposed humus and sharp sand, together with a sprinkling of limestone chippings. Choose a sunny position and water moderately from April to October, with the application of a liquid feed every 4 weeks. In winter, the plants

*Weberocereus tonduzii*

should be kept dry and a minimum temperature of 10°C (50°F) maintained.

### W. fascicularis

The type species was earlier described by E.H.F. Meyer in 1833 as *Cereus fascicularis* and for a while included in *Trichocereus*. The erect stems develop many branches from the base to form thick bushy clusters, about 3 m (10 ft) high, each branch 6 cm (2½ in) thick with about 16 low rounded ribs, pale green in colour. The thick, brown-felted areoles bear numerous yellowish-brown radial spines, about 1 cm, (⅜ in) long, and one long thick central to 4 cm (1½ in). Flowers appear from the tops of the stems; they are approximately 10 cm (4 in) long, reddish-pink on the outside, the inner petals white with brownish edges.

### W. rauhii

A tree-like species from southern Peru, this was discovered and named by Backeberg. It has a short thick trunk, growing to about 6 m (20 ft) tall and branching freely. The thick greyish-green branches have 20 or more ribs with elongating greyish-felted areoles carrying 60–70 greyish silvery radial spines about 1 cm (⅜ in) long and 4–6 yellowish-brown centrals, 2–8 cm (¾–3 in) in length. The flowers, which are 10 cm (4 in) long, open to 4 cm (1½ in) across; they are creamy reddish-brown in colour.

# WEBEROCEREUS

A genus of interesting rain-forest plants, which in recent years has seen an increase in the number of species due to the inclusion of *Werckleocereus* and *Eccremocactus*. It was established in 1909 by Britton and Rose, and named after the French botanist F. Albert Weber, who contributed greatly to the knowledge of cactus plants. All species are epiphytes, growing on trees, with pendent or climbing stems and branches, smooth and cylindrical, angled or thick, flat and leaf-like. They are nocturnal-flowering.

The plants require care in cultivation, humidity being one of their main requirements. They should be grown in a proprietary cactus compost or a peat-based compost to which a third of the bulk in sharp gritty sand has been added. Pot the plants firmly and position them in a well-lit site, out of direct sun, where the branches can either climb or droop from hanging-baskets. The plants should be watered regularly throughout the growing season, and give a liquid fertilizer every 3–4 weeks. In winter keep the compost just moist and maintain a temperature of 18°C (65°F). Propagation is by cuttings in summer.

*Weberocereus bradei*

## W. biolleyi

Originally named by Weber as *Rhipsalis*, this was re-classified by Britton and Rose to become the type species. Known only from Costa Rica, it has very long and slender branches, more or less cylindrical and only about 6 mm ($\frac{1}{4}$ in) in diameter. Areoles are few and far apart, sometimes bearing two or three yellowish spines. The flowers are pink (the inner petals paler than the outer) and about 3–5 cm ($1\frac{1}{4}$–2 in) long. It will climb if placed in close proximity to taller growing plants, otherwise it is a suitable plant for a hanging-basket.

## W. tonduzii

Placed within *Cereus* by Weber, this was later transferred by Britton and Rose to their new genus, *Werckleocereus*, where it remained until David Hunt united it with *Weberocereus*. Recorded only in Costa Rica, this is a plant with stout three-angled stems and branches, the angles often rounded and toothed and carrying aerial roots which support a climbing habit; the areoles are small, rarely with a few weak spines. The flowers, which are about 8 cm (3 in) long and 6 cm ($2\frac{1}{2}$ in) across, are freely borne; the ovary is conspicuous with blackish spines and wool which extends into the tube. The outer petals, approximately 2 cm ($\frac{3}{4}$ in) long, are pinkish-brown, the inner ones, slightly longer, which are creamy-white.

## W. bradei

Also from Costa Rica, this is the erstwhile *Eccremocactus bradei*, a title raised by Britton and Rose in 1913 for this single species, which had previously been known as *Phyllocactus*. The specific name honours Alfred Brade, who introduced the plant in 1906. It has large, thick and flat branches of dull green, usually well in excess of 30 cm (1 ft) in length and up to 10 cm (4 in) across. Spines are borne on marginal areoles, but are generally quite short. Flowers, nearly 8 cm (3 in) long, are pale pinkish-white in colour and of fleshy texture; they last only one night and are followed by carmine-red fruits.

# WEINGARTIA

Much research has been undertaken in respect of this genus, which was established by Werdemann in 1939, the name paying tribute to Wilhelm Weingart the German cactus authority. Many proposals have been made as to the position of the plants within Cactaceae, and it still remains unclear. The genus is a close ally of *Sulcorebutia* and, perhaps to a lesser degree, of *Rebutia* and *Echinopsis*. It seems probable that *Weingartia* will ultimately be absorbed into one of these genera. The species are found in the Andes, in Argentina and Bolivia, and all are globular plants, sometimes partially elongated but remaining solitary. One authority, John Donald, divides the genus into species with raised, round areoles and terminal flowers, and those with more flattened, oval areoles and flowers produced laterally, often several to an areole. The flowers are mainly in shades of yellow but others have been recorded with purplish blooms. Cultivation is not difficult as long as the plants' essential needs are met: a bright and sunny position, a slightly acid, porous compost, careful watering throughout the growing and flowering seasons, with a brief drying-out period between waterings, and feeding every three or four weeks with a weak liquid fertilizer during the summer. Keep the plants dry throughout dormancy, at a minimum temperature of 10°C (50°F). Propagate by seeds early in the year.

## W. neocumingii

This has been a rather confusing species ever since it was first described by Salm-Dyck as *Echinocactus cumingii* in 1850. It has been included within *Lobivia*, *Oroya*, *Spegazzinia*, *Bridgesia* and *Gymnantha* with the same specific epithet, and within *Gymnocalycium* as *neocumingii*. It comes from Florida in Bolivia. It is more or less globular, about 10 cm (4 in) in diameter, with tuberculate ribs spirally arranged. Areoles bear 20 or more pale yellowish radial spines, 1 cm ($\frac{3}{8}$ in) long, and 2–8 brownish, slightly longer centrals which often develop minute hairs. Flowers are borne in the crown; they are bright orange-yellow in colour, funnel-shaped and 3 cm ($1\frac{1}{4}$ in) in length. Several previously recognized species have now been classified as varieties of *W. neocumingii*.

## W. lanata

From Chuquisaca in Bolivia, the species was described by Ritter in 1961. It is a larger species, about 17 cm ($6\frac{3}{4}$ in) thick, with elongated areoles, each with about 15 yellowish-brown radial spines, 4 cm ($1\frac{1}{2}$ in) long, and an equal number of similarly coloured centrals, 5 cm (2 in) long. The flowers, which are bright yellow, are nearly 4 cm ($1\frac{1}{2}$ in) long and 3 cm ($1\frac{1}{4}$ in) across. Donald looks upon certain species in *Weingartia*, such as *W. longigibba*, *W. riograndensis* and *W. pilcomayensis*, as subspecies of *W. lanata*.

## W. neumanniana

First described by Backeberg as *Echinocactus neumanniana* in 1933 and reclassified by Werdermann in this genus in 1937, this is endemic to the Argentinian region of Jujuy. It is a small plant, with a long taproot and a greyish-green body about 5 cm (2 in) wide and 7 cm ($2\frac{3}{4}$ in) high, with areoles set about 1 cm ($\frac{3}{8}$ in) apart, each carrying 6 reddish-brown radial spines about 2 cm ($\frac{3}{4}$ in) long, and one slightly longer central. The flowers, which are yellow-orangy-red, are 2.5 cm (1 in) long.

# WILCOXIA

This genus, containing tuberous-rooted plants found in parts of California, Texas and Mexico, was established by Britton and Rose in 1909 and is named for General Timothy Wilcox, an enthusiast for desert plants. It is now doubtful whether the few species the genus contains will remain under *Wilcoxia*, as current research suggests that they are so similar in certain respects to plants of *Echinocereus* as to be inseparable. They do differ in having elongated, thin stems and branches which in some species reach 1 m (3 ft 3 in) or more in length, spreading and clambering among the desert scrub in which they grow. In cultivation they offer few problems; they flourish if given a bright location out of direct midday sun. A porous cactus compost is essential or the dahlia-like tubers may rot. Some cactus growers graft small branches on to other cacti, such as *Selenicereus* or young plants of *Pachycereus*, but this is unnecessary if care is taken to provide a well-drained growing mixture. Water in moderation during the growing season, but let the compost dry out completely during dormancy from October to early April, and maintain a temperature of 10°C (50°F). Propagate from cuttings in summer or from seeds sown in late winter.

*Weingartia lanata*

### W. viperana

Placed in the genus *Cereus* until Britton and Rose raised the present title and made it the type species. Native to Puebla in Mexico, the species has very long, soft, hairy stems, 1 m (3¼ ft) or more in length and only 2 cm (¾ in) thick at the base, even more slender above. The hairiness gives the stems a reddish-brown appearance. They have 8–10 velvety ribs with regularly spaced areoles bearing about 8 appressed black radial spines, only 2 mm ($\frac{1}{16}$ in) long, and 3–4 downward-pointing central spines. Flowers are borne in profusion along the length of the stems; they are pale reddish in colour, about 8 cm (3 in) long and about 4 cm (1½ in) across when fully open; the petals become reflexed after the first day. Each flower is carried on a long blackish and bristly tube which provides an important feature.

### W. albiflora

This comes from scrub country on the shores of the Gulf of California, south of Guaymas in Mexico. Described by Backeberg, it is a delicate branching plant, with stems about 20 cm (8 in) long and 6 mm (¼ in) thick, greyish-green in colour and with 10–12 ribs covered with many fine whitish, appressed spines. Long-lasting flowers, produced in abundance, are either terminal or borne near the tips of the branches; they are white with greenish-brown throats and a green-tipped style.

*Wilcoxia viperana*

### W. poselgeri

From Texas and Coahuila in Mexico, this is one of the better-known species. It was initially included in the genus *Cereus* and later in *Echinocereus* before being incorporated within *Wilcoxia* in 1909. It is a tall, erect-growing plant of almost bushy habit, arising from a fleshy, black rootstock whose tubers almost surface at times. Branches can attain 60 cm (2 ft) or more in length and are about 1 cm ($\frac{3}{8}$ in) thick, with 8–10 very shallow ribs covered with minute spreading radial and central spines, all greyish-white. The flowers, which generally last for 4–5 days, are usually about 5 cm (2 in) long, pale purplish-pink with deeper colouring in the throat, with creamy-white stamens and a protruding green style and stigma lobes. The oval fruits that follow are pale green in colour.

# WILMATTEA

This small genus of epiphytic plants native to Guatemala and Honduras was established by Britton and Rose in 1920, honouring Ms Wilmatte P. Cockerill an American plant explorer. There is a close relationship with *Hylocereus*, and the species are included in that genus by some authorities, perhaps with justification. They are more or less climbing plants with angled stems and fairly small flowers.

In cultivation they require a very acid compost – with plenty of well-decomposed humus. The plants do best in a shaded position; if they are given too much sun, the colouring of the stems will be adversely affected. Maintain a temperature of 18°C (65°F) at all times as flowers can occur at almost any time of the year. Careful watering is required to ensure that the compost is kept just moist; spray daily with tepid water when the flower buds appear. Feeding should not be necessary unless the soil is poor in humus, but if it does prove necessary, a dilute liquid fertilizer should be applied at monthly intervals.

In a fairly enclosed environment where quite high

humidity can be sustained, these species can prove an interesting addition to other epiphytic plants, such as *Epiphyllum* and *Schlumbergera* (see pages 66–9 and 134–6). Propagation of *Wilmattea* is from cuttings taken in summer.

### W. minutiflora

This was previously described by Britton and Rose as *Hylocereus* and by Vaupel as *Cereus*, both in 1913. It is a very slender three-angled, dark green plant which clambers high into trees and over rocks by means of aerial roots; stems and branches are unlikely to exceed 2 cm ($\frac{3}{4}$ in) in width. Areoles are set about 4 cm ($1\frac{1}{2}$ in) apart along the margins of the stems and carry 2–4 almost minute brownish spines. The small nocturnal flowers, which are approximately 5 cm (2 in) in length, are sweetly scented; the narrow outer segments are a reddish colour, and the inner petals, and the style and stamens are white.

*Wittiocactus amazonicus*

# WITTIOCACTUS

For many years this genus has been recognized under the name *Wittia*, which was established by K. Schumann in 1903 and honoured the Brazilian plant collector N.H. Witt. However, in 1982 it was discovered that this name was already in use for plants of another family, and, following a proposal by S. Rauschert, the generic name of *Wittiocactus* was adopted. This small genus of only two species is localized in mountainous areas of Panama and northern parts of South America, particularly Peru, Colombia and possibly Venezuela, where it grows epiphytically on trees and rocks. It has a close affinity with *Pseudorhipsalis*. The species are a fairly uncommon group in cultivation and may well be considered connoisseur's plants. They need a free-draining compost enriched with plenty of thoroughly decomposed leaf-mould. They do best in a well-lit position, but out of full sunshine and set firmly in hanging-baskets. Regular watering is required during the growing period, and an occasional light spray with tepid water in winter.

Temperatures play an important part in successful flowering, with 15°C (60°F) considered a minimum, and anything higher more beneficial. Fertilize every two or three weeks from April to September. Propagation is by cuttings in summer.

### W. amazonicus

This, the type species, comes the Amazonas regions of Peru and Colombia. It has flat branches with prominent midribs 30 cm (6 in) or more long and about 8 cm (3 in) wide, very leaf-like and regularly notched along the margins. The areoles set within the crenations are spineless, but flowers are borne from almost any areole from the base to the tip of the branches. Appearing in late winter and early spring, they are about 2.5 cm (1 in) long, almost tubular except for the tips of the petals, which spread slightly; the colour is generally pinkish, but turning a deeper shade, and to almost blue in the upper part of the petals. This is possibly the nearest approach to a blue-coloured flower to be found within Cactaceae. Fruits are angular and berry-like, about 1.5 cm ($\frac{5}{8}$ in) long.

### W. panamensis

From Panama and Colombia, and named by Britton and Rose in 1913, this is very similar in most respects to *W. amazonicus*. The branches are flat, with crenate margins, and they often reach to nearly 1 m (3 ft 3 in) in length. The purplish-pink flowers, with deeper colouring at the petal tips, and approximately 3 cm ($1\frac{1}{4}$ in) in length, are borne chiefly towards the upper part of the branches.

# GLOSSARY

**Acute** terminating with a point; pointed

**Areole** a restricted, cushion-like area from which spines and flowers arise

**Axil** the upper angle formed between stem and branch and any other growth arising from it

**Bract** a modified leaf which subtends the flower; a scale-like leaf

**Caespitose** growing in tufts or clumps

**Callus** the tissue that forms over a cut surface

**Campanulate** shaped like a bell

**Cephalium** a crown-like growth or head that forms on certain cacti and from which flowers develop

**Ciliate** being fringed with hairs

**Clavate** shaped like a club

**Cordate** shaped like a heart

**Crenate** with notched, rounded margins

**Cristate** forming a crest; a fasciation

**Dimorphic** appearing in two distinct forms

**Endemic** native to; restricted to a certain area or country

**Epiphyte** a plant growing on other plants, but not parasitic

**Glabrous** smooth; without hairs

**Glaucous** covered with a wax-like bloom

**Glochids** barbed hairs or fine bristles

**Keel** a projecting ridge sometimes occurring on the under-surface of leaves

**Lacerate** torn; deeply cut

**Lanate** woolly

**Lanceolate** shaped like a lance

**Latex** a milky fluid or sap

**Monstrosus** abnormal growth

**Pectinate** fashioned like a comb

**Peltate** shaped like a shield

**Pilose** with soft slender, often minute hairs

**Plicate** folded

**Plumose** feathery

**Pruinose** covered with a waxy bloom

**Pseudocephalium** a false cephalium, usually produced on only one side of a stem

**Rib** a ridge extending longitudinally on a stem

**Saxicolous** growing on, or in close proximity to, rocks

**Serrate** saw-edged

**Spine** a hard pointed growth emerging from the areole; in cacti considered to be a modification of a leaf

**Tomentose** densely woolly

**Truncate** square at the tips

**Tubercle** a small, generally conical, wart-like protuberance

**Tunicate** having multiple layers

**Undulate** having wavy edges

**Xerophyte** a plant capable of withstanding long periods of drought, often possessing peculiar devices to withstand extreme transpiration

**Zygomorphic** having a single symmetrical plane, even when divided into distinctive halves

# BIBLIOGRAPHY

Backeberg C., *Die Cactaceae*, Jena, 1958–62

—, *Cactus Lexicon*, Blandford, Poole, 1976

Britton, N.L. and Rose, J.N., *The Cactaceae*, New York, 1963

Cullmann, Götz and Gröner, *The Encyclopedia of Cacti*, Alphabooks, Sherborne, Dorset, 1986

Donald, J.D., Taxonomic reviews, in *Ashingtonia*, volumes 1–3, Holly Gate, Ashington, Sussex, 1973–8

Hunt D.R., 'Cactaceae' in *The Genera of Flowering Plants*, Hutchinson J., Oxford, 1967

Ritter, F., *Kakteen in Sudamerika*, 4 volumes, Spangenberg, 1979–81

*Repertorium Plantarum Succulentarum*, I.O.S. publication, 1973–85

Rowley, G., *Illustrated Encyclopedia of Succulents*, Salamander Books, London, 1981

# PICTURE CREDITS

All photographs were taken by, and are the copyright of, Peter Stiles except for those on pages 8, 27, 30 (left), 42, 46, 47, 48, 49 (left and right), 50, 56, 57, 71 (bottom), 73 (top), 81, 90, 109, 115, 120, 128, 135, 139 (top and bottom), 141, 148, 149 and 153, which were taken by the author and are copyright Holly Gate International.

# INDEX